THE ENVIRONMENT IN
MODERN PHYSICS

THE ENVIRONMENT
IN
MODERN PHYSICS

A study in relativistic mechanics

C. W. KILMISTER

M.SC., PH.D.

Reader in Applied Mathematics,
King's College, University of London

NEW YORK
AMERICAN ELSEVIER PUBLISHING COMPANY, INC.

First printed 1965

AMERICAN ELSEVIER PUBLISHING COMPANY, INC.
52 Vanderbilt Avenue
New York 17, New York

LIBRARY OF CONGRESS CATALOG CARD NUMBER 65–16709

PRINTED AND BOUND IN GREAT BRITAIN AT
THE PITMAN PRESS, BATH

GENERAL EDITOR'S FOREWORD

by

SIR GRAHAM SUTTON, C.B.E., D.SC., F.R.S.

Director-General, Meteorological Office
Chairman of the National Environment Research Council
Formerly Dean of the Royal Military College of Science, Shrivenham,
and Bashforth Professor of Mathematical Physics

An introduction to the theory of relativity now forms part of most university courses in physics, but the subtlety of the ideas often presents difficulties to the student. The importance of Einstein's work lies more in its theoretical implications than in its practical applications, but the physicist often meets arguments that involve an understanding of the basic concepts of relativistic mechanics.

In this book Dr. Kilmister has dealt with the impact of relativity on modern physics in a novel way. From the starting point of simple and familiar experiments he proceeds, without using elaborate mathematics, to demonstrate a coherence of ideas that began with a view of the macroscopic aspects of the universe and now have relevance for its smallest components, the elementary particles. I believe that a perusal of this fascinating and in many ways highly original book will help the reader to a deeper understanding of modern physical science.

v

INTRODUCTION

It is always possible to look at any scientific theory worthy of the name in a number of different ways. This book is devoted to studying a number of parts of modern physics from a single standpoint, that is, as investigations of the interaction of a system and its environment. The most striking instances of this are the study of elementary particles in which the environment is the most abstract and simple one possible, that is, another elementary particle, and in the study of cosmology where the environment, although given artificially simple properties, is in fact the whole physical universe. In between these two extremes we shall find a number of other instances of theories which can be readily understood in terms of these fruitful ideas of system and environment. The following treatment owes a great deal to my discussions with various workers in the subjects, but particularly to H. Bondi and E. W. Bastin. My thanks are due to them for many stimulating ideas.

C. W. KILMISTER

CONTENTS

Figure 40 is between pages 88 and 89.
All other Figures are in the text.

CHAPTER 1

SYSTEM AND ENVIRONMENT

Environment in Heat

It is a commonplace in physics to study systems interacting with their surroundings, and indeed the whole basis of the scientific method is to divide a complicated problem into parts which interact with one another, and then to concentrate attention on one part of the system and make simplifying assumptions about all the others, which we shall call the environment. This chapter is devoted to a discussion of various instances of this in physics, most of which will not be mentioned again in the later part of the book but are included here to show the widespread application of this analysis.

Let us commence with two instances in heat. The most elementary one which any student of physics encounters very early in his career is that known as the method of mixtures. In one experiment of this kind a piece of lead is weighed, is then hung in boiling water for a good while, and is then swiftly transferred to water at a measured temperature in a well insulated container. The rise in temperature of this water due to the heat carried by the lead is measured, and a quantity called the specific heat of lead is calculated. To put it in the terms of our analysis, the lead is originally in an environment whose properties are specified entirely (as far as this experiment is concerned) by one number—its temperature. It is then transferred to the other container, and here it modifies the environment by raising the temperature of the water. The extent of its ability to modify its environment is measured by its specific heat.

The calculations are usually performed in the following way: Originally the lead is at $100°$ C, and the second container of water is at room temperature $T°$ C. If the final temperature of lead and water is $T_1°$ C, the lead has fallen in temperature by $(100 - T_1)°$, and the water risen by $(T_1 - T)°$. By experiments with different values of T, and different masses of lead, it transpires that there is a constant S such that, if W_l, W are the weights of lead and fluid, then

$$SW_l(100 - T_1) = W(T_1 - T)$$

and this quantity S is the specific heat. (In the usual description of the experiment the specific heat measures the quantity of heat involved in raising the temperature of the lead to $100°$ centigrade, but our description does not involve the slightly mystical concept of quantity

1

of heat, although we do have to introduce the idea of the power of the lead in modifying its environment).

Stefan's Law

The second instance in heat which repays analysis is a little more complicated. Heated bodies radiate, and if two bodies of different temperatures are near each other, there is a net flow of energy from that at a higher temperature to that at a lower. At first sight it seems as if our analysis would have the form of looking at one body, say the hotter one, as the system, and regarding the cooler one as the environment, but this turns out to be unfruitful. Instead physicists have learnt that it is best to describe radiation in terms of all bodies radiating, but with hotter bodies radiating more energy than colder ones, so that there is, on balance, a net transfer of energy from hotter to colder bodies. The question then is how much energy a body radiates at a certain temperature, and this is answered by Stefan's law that every body, at an absolute temperature T, radiates energy proportionally to the fourth power of T. (The absolute temperature scale is that derived by theoretical considerations and it is related to the centigrade scale by the relation:- absolute temperature equals centigrade temperature $+273$). We may here regard Stefan's law as an empirical law, although in fact it can be derived from more fundamental considerations by thermo-dynamics. The analysis in terms of environment is now considerably more subtle. The system, that is the radiating body, is described by a single parameter, the temperature, and the environment consists of all the other bodies, each described by their temperatures.

Optical Results

We now come to similar analyses of experiments in optics. Here again one of the first things that any student of physics learns in optics is the phenomenon of refraction. In elementary optics light is regarded as some kind of transfer of energy whose exact nature does not need to be specified, but whose operation in a certain environment is again determined by a single parameter called the refractive index of the environment. This way of looking at things is most strikingly exhibited if we express optics in the form of Fermat's Principle of "least time". The velocity of light in a medium of refractive index n is inversely proportional to n, so that the time taken by the light to go from one point to another is proportional to n and to the distance between the points. The Principle of Fermat is that the path of light through the environment is so determined as to make the total time a minimum. For example, consider (*Figure 1*) light passing from a source S in a medium of refractive index l to a receiver R in a medium of refractive index m separated from the first medium by a plane face. So long as the light is travelling in only one of the two media, its path by Fermat's Principle will

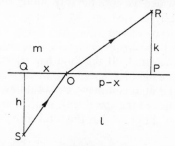

Figure 1

obviously be a straight line, and so we have only to determine at what point of the interface the light crosses to make the total time a minimum for the two straight line paths which join S and R.

Figure 2 shows a slightly altered path of the light; if SOR is a path of least time, then to the first order of small quantities $SO'R$

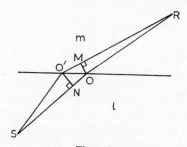

Figure 2

must give the same time. Since the velocity is inversely proportional to the refractive index, this means that the time saved by not having to traverse NO, l. NO, is equal to that lost in travelling along $O'M$, m. $O'M$. Hence also, in the minimum position

$$l\frac{NO}{OO'} = m\frac{O'M}{OO'}$$

which is the same as

$$l\frac{x}{\sqrt{x^2 + h^2}} = m\frac{p - x}{\sqrt{k^2 + (p - x)^2}},$$

known as *Snell's law*.

Fresnel's Experiment

Just as with the two examples in heat, we now come to another optical problem which is considerably more subtle. This is the experiment originally carried out by Fresnel, in which a beam of light is passed down a long tube containing fluid which moves through the tube with speed v (*Figure 3*). The resulting speed of the beam of light is measured. If the fluid has refractive index n then, when it is at rest, the light has speed c/n, where c is the speed of light in vacuo. When the fluid is moving we would expect the speed v to make some difference to the speed with which the light travels along the tube and one might guess that the total speed would be obtained

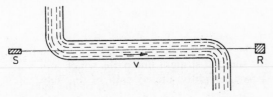

Figure 3   Schematic diagram of Fresnel's experiment.

simply by adding v to c/n. However, this cannot be the case, for if it were we could imagine a whole series of such experiments in which the fluid was replaced by gases at lower and lower density so that their refractive indices became nearer and nearer to 1, and in each of these cases the speed would still be obtained by adding v to the speed of light in the medium of rest. But by continuing in this way we would eventually arrive at the paradoxical situation in which nothing at all is passing through the tube and yet the light still travels more quickly along it. So it is clear that if the velocity v is involved it must be modified by some property of the environment, that is, of the fluid, which will cause the velocity to have very little effect when the environment has a refractive index very near to 1. The actual formula found experimentally was in fact

$$\frac{c}{n} + v\left(1 - \frac{1}{n^2}\right)$$

which exactly fulfils the conditions which we have found. This example of the effect of the environment on the transmission of light is particularly interesting as it was one of the outstanding experiments at the end of the nineteenth century whose subsequent explanation (in this case by the special theory of relativity) initiated the scientific revolution of our present century.

Black-body Radiation

Now that we have considered some experiments in heat and in optics let us go on to ask some questions about what happens when these two subjects are combined. Everyone has observed that a poker which has been in a hot fire emits a red glow when it is taken out. Moreover, the colour of the glow depends on the heat of the fire, and how long the poker has been in. In fact, it depends on the temperature of the poker; from the point of view of this book the fire is simply specified by a single parameter, its temperature, and this temperature is communicated to the poker. A more scientific way of investigating this connection between light and heat is to

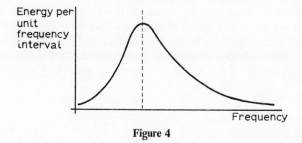

Figure 4

construct a totally enclosed metal box, one side of which has a very small hole through which the inside of the box can be observed. The box is now heated to a high temperature, say by Bunsen burners, and as the temperature rises the colour of the inside of the box is observed. What is found is not light of one particular frequency, that is to say the radiation has not one specific colour, but a distribution of energy in the radiation over the frequency range of a general form like that shown in *Figure 4*. As the temperature rises the peak of the curve moves to a higher frequency.

The theoretical problem now before us is to determine this distribution of energy against frequency in the radiation which is in equilibrium with matter at a certain temperature. This was another of the problems which, at the turn of the century, led to the revolution in physics. It is worth considering this problem a little more here, although it belongs to the history of a part of physics of which we are considering a more modern version in detail later in this book, that is, quantum mechanics. The position at the end of the nineteenth century was that the electro-magnetic theory of light had had considerable success. This theory describes light as the same kind of radiation as radio waves, the only difference being that light is of a higher frequency, and each of these radiations were adequately described by a set of equations found by Maxwell in 1864 and always called after him. To be more precise, the general behaviour of radiation was well described by Maxwell's equations but they offered no help in this present problem for they made no mention of temperature at all. Here was an instance of a theory which purported to describe a physical system, in this case radiation, but which had omitted to provide for the description of the environment of the radiation altogether (that is, it made no provision for incorporating the temperature of the surroundings).

The Doppler Effect

As a last instance of the problems of environment in classical physics we consider the treatment of the Doppler effect in sound. The theory of sound waves is in a very fortunate position because the waves are vibrations in the atmosphere and so there is always at hand a self-evidently satisfactory environment, that is, the still air. When we speak of the speed of sound, we always mean the speed

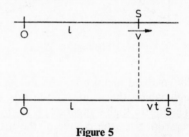

Figure 5

relative to the surrounding air and we never get into any difficulties about environment on that account. Everyone has noticed the Doppler effect, in which sound of a certain pitch appears to change in pitch, depending upon whether the source is moving towards or away from the observer. Because the speed of sound is relative to the air the effect of the source moving towards or away from the observer is quite different from that of the observer moving towards or away from the source. To see this in a simple manner imagine (*Figure 5*) a source S moving with speed v away from an observer O at rest, and let us suppose for simplicity that the source, instead of emitting a steady tone, emits pips of sound at intervals of time t. If one pip is emitted when the source is at a distance l from the observer and so reaches the observer at a time l/c later, where c is the speed of sound, the next pip emitted at time t later has to travel a greater distance, $l + vt$, to the observer and so arrives at a time

$$t + \frac{vt}{c} = \left(1 + \frac{v}{c}\right) t$$

later than the first pip. The intervals between the pips are therefore modified by a factor which depends upon the velocity. Notice that if the velocity is negative and equal to that of sound, all the pips arrive at the observer simultaneously. This is connected with the supersonic bang which has become distressingly familiar. The effect depends on the velocity of the source of sound relative to the air, not on the relative speeds of source and observer. *Figure 6*

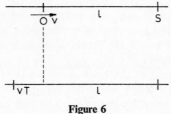

Figure 6

shows the situation in which a source at rest sends pips towards an observer moving away with speed v. If the first pip is emitted at zero time and therefore reaches O at time l/c, the next pip emitted at a time t later has further to travel because the observer at time T is at $-vT$, where T is the time interval between the reception of the two pips.

The interval between the pips at O is therefore $t + \frac{vT}{c} = T$ by

assumption. Hence $T = \frac{t}{1 - v/c}$, and the interval is now modified by a different factor. It is clear from this formula that no question of a supersonic bang can arise in this case. Of course, when v is very small compared with the speed of sound, both formulae give more nearly the same result.

The Environment in General

The problems considered in this chapter have been drawn from various branches of physics to show that the idea of a system reacting with its environment is an extremely common one in physics. The actual problems considered in the rest of the book are those raised in the same way by the environment in a progressively more subtle sense. We begin by considering Newtonian mechanics and see how this leads to a definite picture of the environment, but unfortunately to a picture which contains paradoxes, since the universe it considers is infinite, and also to a picture which conflicts with experience in various branches of physics, notably optics. It turns out to be impossible to consider mechanics properly except in terms of the whole universe because Newton's formulation depends on the existence of certain frames of reference with respect to which his laws hold, and these frames of reference are determined by the most distant matter. We have therefore to consider problems of cosmology, in which the environment is the whole physical universe, whatever this phrase is taken to mean. In order to remove the conflict of Newtonian mechanics with experience we have to do this in a way which is at least consistent with the special theory of relativity. This theory can very profitably be considered as the construction of an abstract kind of environment for mechanical and electrical phenomena and the analysis of this will occupy a fair proportion of the book.

Finally, the last part of the book describes the most subtle use of the concept of environment which has yet appeared, the application to the theory of elementary particles. This has been made recently from a somewhat different point of view by various workers in the field, but it is perhaps most associated with the name of Chew. Here the environment of a particle is quite simply the other particle with which it is interacting in a collision experiment, the only experience from which we have any evidence of these particles. But here the simplicity of both the system and the environment leads to a complete symmetry between the two so that what had been thought of as environment can be described as system and vice versa. The last part of the book shows how this symmetry has important numerical conclusions and in view of the importance of this application the mathematics of it will be described at some length.

CHAPTER 2

ABSOLUTE SPACE

The Mechanical Environment

In the first chapter we considered a number of physical experiments from the point of view of systems interacting with their environments. The examples considered there had in common the property that the environment was a particular one which might have been otherwise; for example, in the experiment to determine the specific heat of lead, the lead was immersed in water at 100° C, but some other liquid which boiled at a different temperature or any other environment of a controlled temperature could have been used. In the rest of this book we are going to be concerned with our environment in a *universal* sense; that is to say, we are concerned with physical systems interacting with environments which could not possibly be otherwise.

The most obvious example of such an environment is the whole universe, considered in cosmology. It makes no sense to talk of the universe possibly being different from what it is; we have to take it as we find it. But the cosmological environment is only the most obvious instance of a universal one we shall find. A number of other such environments are to some extent connected with it. Although the examples in the previous chapter were untypical in dealing with particular environments, they do tell us an important fact about this way of treating physics. In each case the environment was so simplified that it could be described by a single number, for instance, in the case of the heat experiments, by the temperature. We are not going to attempt in this book to define exactly what we mean by environment, but one characteristic which is always present in this analysis is the simplicity assumed of the environment so that it can always be described either by a single number or by one or two numbers.

By far the commonest physical phenomena in our world are mechanical, and this was true even before our present highly mechanised age. One of the most pressing problems for the ancient natural philosophers was the explanation of the motion of the stars and of the planets. Not only was this of great interest to the curious mind, impressed by the beauty of the heavens on a clear night, but it was also of great value in navigation. Such motions were obviously related in some way to mechanical motions on the earth's surface, but the exact nature of this connection was for a long time a mystery. This chapter attempts a historical analysis of the way in which this problem has been tackled in terms of the point of view elaborated earlier. We have, in short, to ask ourselves what is the nature of the environment implied by mechanical explanations of motion.

Newtonian Space

This question is clearly much more subtle than those raised in the discussion of the theory of heat and optics in Chapter 1. The environment in mechanics is to a large extent taken for granted, and we have to disentangle it from a great deal of other material. Before we consider the views of the Greeks about this it would be as well to consider a little of Newton's opinion. We often find in books about mechanics some such phrase as "Newton assumed absolute space". What exactly does this mean? In Newton's great work on mechanics "The Mathematical Principles of Natural Philosophy" he does indeed use the phrase "absolute space" and he introduces it in an exceedingly obscure sentence. Firstly he says "I do not define time, space, place and motion as being well known to all". He then goes on to say that the common people have certain prejudices about these ideas which he wishes to avoid. Then about space he says "absolute space in its own nature without relation to anything external remains always similar and immovable". When somebody as clear sighted and precise as Newton sees fit to write such a sentence it is certainly of interest to enquire just what prompts him to do so and to try and see what he means by it.

Ancient Ideas of Space

Nowadays we are accustomed to using the word space from an early age so that we do not question the ideas which the word is meant to summarise, and we are therefore not in a good position to appreciate the long history of these ideas in man's thought. If we open a modern book which tries to express its ideas about space explicitly, it will contain some such statements as that space is continuous, the same in all directions and the same at all points. However, it is clear that these properties are not to be verified as a result of our sense of perception; they are the result of a long series of progressive refinements of the conception of space, a series of abstractions which begin before the beginning of history. Archeological discoveries have shown that space was originally conceived as being merely a state of accidental relations between objects, and so was something which had a unique significance for each individual man. The next step is when these individual ideas are somehow coordinated with each other and a general idea of space common to a group of people materialises. This new idea is then able to incorporate common important phenomena like sunrise and sunset. Even with the introduction of proper measurement standards, so that lengths and volumes can be compared, it is found that these lengths and volumes are not thought of abstractly. For example, the ancient Sumerian unit of area was the grain, showing that these people thought of area entirely from the point of view of the quantity of seed which was necessary to sow the area in question.

From these very practical ideas of a common space it is a long step forward to that of Lucretius. In his writings we find for the first time a modern idea of space. He begins his treatment of physics by postulating two things with which to describe motion; bodies, and a void in which the bodies move about. This is exactly how we think of space nowadays. But, clear as this seems to us, it was not so clear to the contemporaries and successors of Lucretius, and we find in Aristotle's Physics a very much more careful and detailed treatment of space, but one which is quite at variance with Lucretius and with modern thinking. It would take us too far afield to try to describe the exceedingly complex treatment by Aristotle of the location of bodies and the nature of motion. Suffice it to say that Newton's statement about space can be seen partly as an attempt to clear away mistaken views based on Aristotle's theories.

Returning to Newton, it is worth remarking that he was the first to draw a clear boundary between science and metaphysics. He did not wish to get rid of metaphysics, and indeed we know enough of his life to realise how very much his interests lay in the direction of the metaphysical, the occult and the religious. His intention was merely to keep these things out of his physical investigations because he thought quite clearly that they were irrelevant to science and that to admit them to this field would be a return to the ways of thinking of the Middle Ages. In this programme of keeping science and metaphysics in separate compartments Newton was successful in every respect except for his theory of space.

Newton's Laws of Motion

Before going on it will be as well to refresh our minds about Newton's assumptions on mechanics, that is his laws of motion. He bases his mechanics ostensibly on three laws of motion.

Law 1: every body continues in its state of rest or of uniform motion in a straight line except insofar as it is acted on by forces which change its motion. Law 2: the rate of change of motion of the body is the measure of the force acting upon it, and takes place in the direction in which the force acts. Law 3: if two bodies act on each other then the force which the first exerts on the second is equal and opposite to that which the second exerts on the first, and both these forces are along the line joining the bodies. We had better be clear straight away that there is much more in these laws than meets the eye. The first one appears to say that bodies move in a certain way except insofar as they don't; if they are not moving uniformly in a straight line then one says that a force is acting. The second law then tells one how to put a numerical measure on to forces and from this point of view only the third law really states anything new about the outside world. Now this essentially trivial interpretation of the laws of motion cannot possibly be right, no matter how plausible it seems, because mechanics is so exceedingly successful in explaining all the complicated phenomena around us. We can only understand the whole content of Newton's laws if we try to put ourselves in the historical position that Newton was in and try to see what he was denying in asserting these things, and if we try to see what hidden assumptions the laws rest on. Here we shall be mainly concerned with the first law and we can at once see one interesting assumption that it makes. It asserts the equivalence of a state of rest and a state of uniform motion, that is, motion with a constant speed in a straight line. It is perfectly possible in modern jet aircraft to stand a penny on its edge on a table, or, indeed, if the aircraft companies could be persuaded to provide the apparatus, it would be perfectly possible to play billiards in just the same way as on the surface of the earth. Secondly, and to some extent as a corollary of this, the first law states that if we have something moving uniformly it is quite unnecessary to look for anything causing the motion. This was a great step forward from the mechanics of Aristotle, who thought that uniform motion required a cause. Newton realised the value of the first law although it was already current before he wrote and can certainly be traced back to Galileo in 1638. We are now in a better position to realise Newton's quandary over space and his need for a discussion of absolute and relative space. In order to express the first law of motion in the way in which he had expressed it, he had to have some absolute standard of rest from which to view the body as moving uniformly. From the point of view of his philosophy Newton could not conceive of anything but an absolute space, but the difficulty which he found himself in was that his first law did not define this absolute space but in fact left a considerable freedom. There is a whole class of relative spaces defined by the first law.

Motion

The Greeks were very concerned with the nature of space, as we have just seen, and the reason for this concern was because they felt that space held the clue to the phenomenon of motion. Motion is now an idea which we take for granted, relying on our earliest perceptions to tell us all we need to know about it, and avoiding any deeper probing. For the Greeks it was not so; amongst other paradoxes to do with motion which troubled them we may pick out the "Arrow" of Zeno (495–435 B.C.). He considers an arrow flying from A to B: before it can reach B it must first reach a point C half-way between A and B. Before it can reach C it must reach a

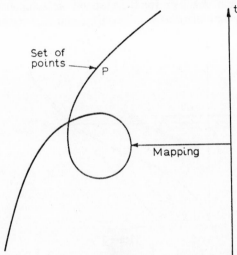

Figure 7

point D half-way between A and C; and so on. Proceeding in this way we reach the conclusion that the arrow can never move.

We see at once the great step forward made by Galileo and Newton and their contemporaries. It is not that questions like Zeno's are answered, at least at the beginning of the subject; it is that they are ignored, as they should be, until sufficient mathematical apparatus has been developed to deal with them. Instead motion is taken for granted; one considers a set of points in space arranged along a curve (*Figure 7*), and to each point one associates a particular value of a parameter t, called the *time* in such a way that whenever two values of t are very near together the corresponding points of the set are also very close. This is a rough definition of a *continuous mapping*; we ought to make it a little more precise by putting it in the form: at any point P, corresponding to t, we can, if we wish to make sure that points corresponding to other times t' are nearer to P than any previously given magnitude, name a quantity c which will ensure this whenever $t' - t$ is less in magnitude than c. When this has been said, there is no point in further elaboration about the nature of motion; a moving point *is* simply such a set of points.

From our position of advantage it is clear that Newton and Galileo carried this admirable programme out a little too drastically. It was very satisfactory to avoid posing unanswerable philosophical problems about the nature of motion, but the nature of *time* is something that needs a little more investigation. We shall deal with this in the next chapter; for the moment we assume with Newton and Galileo that there is a unique time which everyone will agree

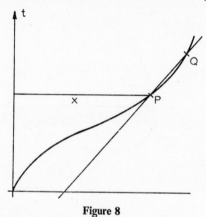

Figure 8

about. The motion of a point P along a straight line can conveniently be represented by a stationary curve in the following way (*Figure 8*). We first draw a line up the page to represent the parameter t, and for each value of t we measure a distance x at right angles, across the page, to represent the distance travelled in that time. (It was at one time more usual to draw t across the page and x up, but the convention used here is now the usual one.) Different motions along the line will be represented by different curves; for example that in *Figure 9* represents a point starting at one point A of the line, moving to the right to a point B, returning to A and then waiting at A until it is time to move off to the left.

The slope of the line from A to C tells us how long the point takes to travel a given distance; to put it another way the ratio $\dfrac{AB}{BC}$ is the distance travelled per unit time, and this is called the speed. Because AC is a straight line it makes no difference whether we find the speed from A to D or D to C i.e. it is uniform. If the line is curved we can still associate a speed with each point by considering the limiting value of the speed associated with a chord *PQ* (*Figure 8*) when *Q* comes very near to *P* (so that the chord becomes very near to a tangent).

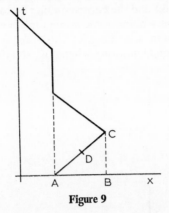

Figure 9

Acceleration

Now Aristotle's view was that a motion like that from *A* to *C* needs a continual explanation; at every point of the path we must seek a cause for the passing on to the next point. The real point of Newton's first law is to deny this view of Aristotle's: to explain a

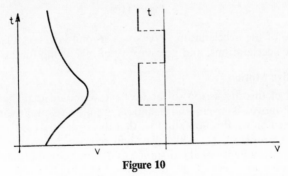

Figure 10

straight path in our figure, according to Newton, it is sufficient to explain why it begins. Once it has left *A* the path will continue straight unless something else happens. What needs explanation, for Newton, is non-uniformity in the velocity or *acceleration*. We can represent the acceleration in a similar diagram by measuring at each time *t* a distance representing the velocity of the point at that time; this device is known as the hodograph. *Figure 10* shows the two hodographs of the motions shown in *Figure 8* and *Figure 9*. We notice that the hodograph of the second motion has discontinuities (jumps); this is because we have idealised the motion by allowing sharp corners in the diagrams of *Figure 9*. In practice these corners would be rounded off and the corresponding hodograph would be as in *Figure 11*. At every point of the hodograph curve we can measure the speed of the point describing it; this speed is the rate at which the speed in the original motion is changing, and this is the numerical

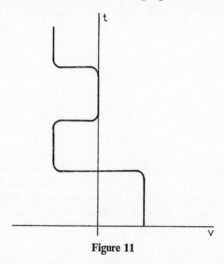

Figure 11

measure of the acceleration. Newton's second law says that forces produce accelerations, and gives a way of measuring forces.

Relative Motion

In all of this discussion so far we have supposed that the line on which P moves is given, and distances are all measured from some point fixed on it. But now suppose that this is not the case; suppose that two people O, Q—which we shall refer to as *observers*—both make measurements of the distance of P, and suppose that O also makes measurements of the distance of Q. For the sake of simplicity let us begin with the case when Q moves uniformly relative to O. The situation is clear from *Figure 12*. If we (arbitrarily) imagine that our picture is drawn from O's viewpoint, so that he is always on the time-axis, then Q will be on a line making a certain angle with this axis. At any time t, measured from the moment when O, Q coincide, we have for Q's measurement of distance

$$QP = OP - OQ$$
$$= OP - Vt$$

where V is the speed of OQ, so that

$$\frac{OQ}{OO_1} = V.$$

If both observers determine the speed of P they derive two different values U_O, U_Q related by

$$U_Q = U_O - V.$$

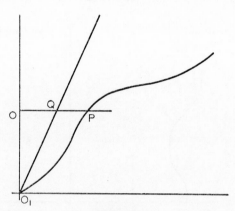

Figure 12

We can then compare the hodographs as drawn by each observer; Q's is a curve looking exactly like O's, but moved to the left by an amount V (*Figure 13*). O and Q therefore *agree* about the acceleration of the point, and therefore (by Newton's laws) about the forces acting.

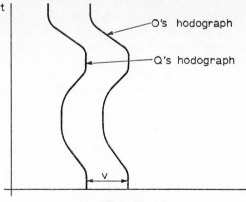

Figure 13

Next consider a different case in which O and P are observers measuring the motion of a particle Q (in the same figure as before). Clearly O measures Q as moving with no acceleration and so under no forces, but the same is not true of P. In fact the two hodographs have the forms shown in *Figure 14*. Thus P measures Q as accelerated. There are now two points of view that one can take; one can stick by Newton's laws, and say that P finds that forces are acting on Q, although O does not. Or one can decide that Newton's laws

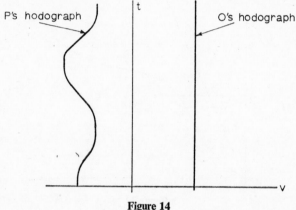

Figure 14

are only true for *some* observers. It was essentially the second choice that necessitated absolute space for Newton, though in fact we realise now that it is not necessary to have *one* absolutely fixed observer. All that is needed is to have this set of observers, any two of which are moving uniformly relative to each other, for all of which Newton's laws are true. These are the *inertial observers*.

Such an observer can measure the acceleration of a particle, and he will then (it is implied by Newton's laws), be able to assign numbers, m, called *masses* to the various particles so that the force F on a particle is measured by the product mf (and is in the same direction as f). The forces defined in this way (*a*) can usually (but not always) be correlated with physically evident things (taut strings, rails &c.), (*b*) are consistent in that they obey the third law of motion.

Once this has been done it is useful to consider, instead of velocity and mass separately, momentum $p = mv$ and energy $E = \frac{1}{2}mv^2$. The rate at which p changes now gives F, whilst the change in E when v changes to $v + h$ is equal to $\frac{1}{2}m[(v + h)^2 - v^2] = mvh$ if h is very small. Thus the rate at which E changes is Fv, which is called the *rate of working of the force F*. The importance of the ideas of energy and work is that they connect mechanics with other branches of physics, because mechanical energy can be transformed into other forms (e.g. heat energy) but the total of all forms of energy remains constant.

The Projectile

And so we can say that the background, that is the environment, which is implied by Newton's laws is not absolute space as Newton thought but the complete set of inertial observers. We ought to notice here, what we said earlier, that the question of the time has

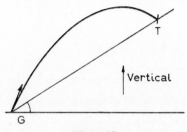

Figure 15

not been fully considered; we have assumed that all the observers have been able to agree about time measurement. It is not only for the theoretical investigation of the principles of mechanics that transformations from one observer to another are useful; it is of interest to solve problems by looking at them from the point of view of the observer with respect to which they are most simple. Consider the problem of determining the greatest range of a gun which is firing up a uniform slope (*Figure 15*). In the usual way of treating this problem one works out in what path the projectile moves, and this is actually the parabola, and then one determines in what direction to shoot the projectile off originally, so that this parabola reaches to the greatest possible distance along the plane. Now this usual way of doing it is from the point of view of an observer who is fixed on the earth, and this observer finds that everything in his immediate neighbourhood has a downward acceleration of approximately 32 feet per second per second. This suggests at once another observer, with respect to whose measurements the motion of the projectile is much more simple, that is, the observer who is himself freely falling with an acceleration 32 feet per second per second. Such an observer, because he is falling with the projectile, sees it acted on by no forces and so he sees it moving in a straight line *GP* (*Figure 16*). Now the only difficulty about this way of treating things is that the target *T*, which was previously at rest for the old observer,

is moving vertically upwards for the new observer, with an acceleration 32 feet per second per second, and so the range of the projectile
is the distance which it can move along its straight line before it is
hit by the upward moving target; or rather the range up the slope
is the distance away of that target which falling freely upward just
strikes the projectile. In order to find out how far away this range
is we need the formula which is not difficult to establish independ-
ently, that something moving from rest for a time t with acceleration g moves a distance $\frac{1}{2}gt^2$.

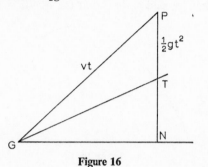

Figure 16

The simplest way of seeing this is to find the acceleration of a
point moving in such a way that at time t it has moved a distance
$x = \frac{1}{2}gt^2$. After time t_1 it has moved a distance x_1 (say) where

$$x_1 = \tfrac{1}{2}gt_1^2,$$
$$\text{and so} \qquad x_1 - x = \tfrac{1}{2}g(t_1^2 - t^2)$$
$$= \tfrac{1}{2}g(t_1 - t)(t_1 + t).$$

The average speed in this interval is then

$$\frac{x_1 - x}{t_1 - t} = g\,\frac{t_1 + t}{2},$$

and so when the interval taken is very short, the velocity v is given
by

$$v = gt.$$

This means that the hodograph is a straight line, and so the acceleration is constant and equal to g. We can then see that the target has
risen distance $\frac{1}{2}gt^2$ in the same time that the projectile has moved a
distance Vt and we have to determine in what direction to move the
projectile so that the distance away of the target is greatest. This is
most easily accomplished by comparing the expression for the square
of the horizontal distance travelled which can be derived in two

different ways by Pythagoras's theorem. If we consider the triangle *GPN* then we have the expression $(Vt)^2 - (h + \frac{1}{2}gt^2)^2$ and from the triangle *GTN* we have that it is $R^2 - h^2$. Comparing these two expressions gives us an equation to determine and this equation is one of the second degree in t^2; that means that there are two solutions, that is two values of the time for any particular distance if there are any at all, with the exception of the case in which the equation has equal roots. There will be equal roots if the points are just within range, no solution for points which are out of range, and for the points well within range there will be two solutions. Writing down the condition for the equal roots of the quadratic equation we see that there is an equation which determines at once the range along the plane, and then using this value for the range it is easy to verify that the direction of projection is the one which bisects the angle between the slope and the vertical. Of course this example is not one of very great importance and it can be solved easily by other methods, but it suffices to show that the method of transforming to another observer is of practical value as well as merely of interest in the foundation of the subject.

Newton's Rotating Pail

Of course, if Newton had been able to free his mind from his philosophically preconceived ideas he would have taken all uniformly moving inertial frames as equivalent to each other, but as he could admit only one absolute space he was obliged to distinguish one of this collection. The only way in which he could do this was a cosmological one. He makes the hypothesis that the centre of the "system of the world" is immovable. This centre is for Newton the centre of gravity of the sun, the earth and the planets. It is surprising that Newton did not here try to take into account the distant stars when trying to find a fixed centre. This is the more surprising since it was only after the death of Newton that the motions of the stars relative to each other was definitely established. The search for absolute space caused Newton to make one of his rare errors. He admits that it is not easy to determine absolute space as distinct from relative space but he says it is not altogether impossible, and he describes his famous pail experiment.

In this experiment a pail is hung from the ceiling by a long cord and the pail is turned so that the cord is twisted. The pail is filled with water and held at rest. When it is allowed to move the cord untwists so that the pail rotates, and as the rotation is communicated to the water the water rises at the side of the pail and falls in the middle giving a concave figure. The fact that the surface of the water is no longer level is taken by Newton as evidence of the absolute nature of rotation. In discussing this experiment Newton assumes that the surface of water in the pail would be just the same if the pail were rotating in empty space instead of the actual universe in which there is a considerable quantity of matter. This assumption is, of course, beyond our ability to verify. If the pail were imagined as at rest and all the matter rotating around it, it is at least as likely that the surface will again be concave as that it will be flat. Thus Newton's experiment is of no assistance in establishing the absolute space which he felt he had to have mainly for religious and philosophical reasons. If we go on to consider Newton's laws and their consequences in more detail we must consider how Newton, and to some extent his predecessors, were able to arrive at these laws. Without some such discussion it is not possible to understand the true significance of the laws and so their implications for the environment.

Kepler's Laws

The greatest help in deriving Newton's laws came from Kepler who announced his laws of planetary motion in 1609. Kepler's laws were laws in a different sense from Newton's; they were merely statements of observed regularities in the motion of the planets without any enquiry into the cause of these motions, whereas, as we have seen, Newton's laws make statements about the forces which cause changes of motion. Kepler's three laws are as follows—

1. The planets move in ellipses with the sun at one focus.
2. The radius vector of each planet sweeps out equal areas in equal times.
3. The squares of the periodic times are proportional to the cubes of the major axes of the ellipses.

It is one of the most astonishing coincidences in the history of science that just these three empirical generalisations provided the necessary information for Newton to formulate his laws of motion and his theory of gravitation. Before we go on to see how Newton's theory follows from Kepler's laws let us observe two significant facts about these laws. Firstly the placing of the sun at one focus of the ellipse suggests that the sun is the common cause of the planets' motions, and we must remember that we see the sun in its position because it is a star and emits light, that is electro-magnetic radiation. If the sun were invisible the cogency of Kepler's laws would be reduced, (supposing they could ever have been discovered) and this is an instance of the fact, which rarely appears in books on mechanics, that there really are no entirely mechanical phenomena; the interest in Kepler's laws arises partly from the electro-magnetic radiation from the sun. Secondly the law of areas, that the radius vector to the planet moves at a certain rate, obviously implies that the observer has some fixed directions at his disposal relative to which he can measure the rotation. These fixed directions for Kepler are the directions to the fixed stars, and so we see that Kepler's second law is not a statement about the solar system alone but a cosmological statement about the whole universe.

Let us now see how Kepler's laws lead to Newton's theory of gravitation. We will assume here Newton's laws of motion, although of course the original problem posed to Newton was to find both the laws of motion and the theory of gravitation.

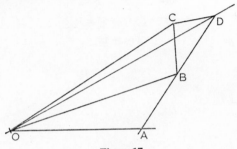

Figure 17

The very beautiful treatment given by Newton of the law of areas is as follows: First, to show that a body moving under a force passing always through a fixed point O traces out equal areas in equal times, suppose A, B, C be three successive nearby points through which the body passes, the very short intervals of time from A to B and B to C being equal (*Figure 17*). If there were no force in action, the body would (by the first law) continue to D, where $AB = BD$. But the force along OB causes a change of motion and this change is parallel to OB. So that CD is parallel to OB and therefore the triangles COD, CBD are equal in area i.e.

$$\Delta OAB = \Delta OBD = \Delta OBC - \Delta OCD + \Delta BCD = \Delta OBC.$$

Since this argument is true for any part of the trajectory, however short, the law of areas follows.

Conversely if the law of areas is true this argument can be reversed to prove that CD and OB are parallel, and so the law of force is a central one.

Determination of the Inverse Square Law: 1

It is very instructive to see how Newton presented the original discussions of the further consequences of Kepler's laws. The geometrical analysis above which proves that when the orbit is such that equal areas are swept out in equal times it is taking place under a force towards the centre (about which the equal areas are described), is a very simple one. The appropriate work for determining the actual law of force is a good deal more complicated. Newton

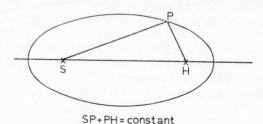

SP+PH = constant

Figure 18

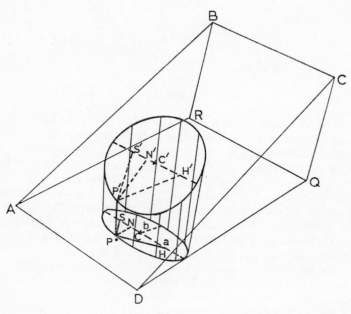

Figure 19

undoubtedly had various powerful methods for doing this which he felt it was inappropriate to explain to his contemporaries at this stage; his great work is entirely in geometrical terms, although it is inconceivable that even someone of Newton's genius could have discovered all the results in that way. Kepler's laws state, as we have seen, that the orbits of the planets are ellipses with the sun at one focus. One definition of an ellipse, which enables us to understand this law a little more easily, is that it is the locus of a point which moves so that the sum of its distances from two fixed points which are called the foci, is constant (*Figure 18*). This is the gardener's method of drawing an elliptical flower bed, with two posts and a length of string passing round them. The sun is at one focus of the ellipse and there is nothing at the other focus. With respect to the sun the radius vector to the particle sweeps out equal areas in equal times, according to the other one of Kepler's laws. For our purposes it is better to take the definition of the ellipse as the projection of a circle by orthogonal projection; that is to say, we imagine a circle drawn on a plane *ABCD* and then perpendiculars let fall from every point of the plane on to another plane *ADRQ* inclined at a certain angle to the first one (*Figure 19*), and it is then well known (and not difficult to prove) that the feet of these perpendiculars generate an ellipse.

With this definition of an ellipse we can give a simpler proof of Newton's results which will still give the general feel of his argument but will not require from the reader such an extensive knowledge of geometrical conics as he assumed. He first considers several subsidiary problems which will enable him to answer the main one and we will take these in turn.

Determination of the Inverse Square Law: 2

Firstly it is clear that a circle may be described under any law of force whatever towards the centre so long as the magnitude of the speed is an appropriate one, for the law of force can depend on the distance from the centre, and therefore is constant at all parts of the circle so that the circle may be described uniformly. It therefore follows that in particular a circle may be described under the law of force proportional to the distance from the centre of force. This is a law of force often considered by mathematicians in doing problems about central forces; of course, it is one which could never be observed experimentally, for if the law increases as we get away from the centre of force the most distant matter in the universe would have a very predominant effect, and we shall never be able to alter circumstances sufficiently to make any measurements. However, for the purposes of the calculation we may suppose such a law of force to exist, and a circle to be described under this direct distance law. If we now suppose the circle projected into an ellipse by orthogonal projection, the distances along one axis of the ellipse will be reduced in size, while those along the other axis will be left unchanged. If we suppose that the forces follow the same rule, so that the force on the particle is still along the radius vector to the

centre, and is proportional to the distance to the centre, it is fairly
clear from the orthogonal projection that this law of force will be
one which enables the ellipse to be described. We have then the
fact that an ellipse described under a central force towards the centre
is so described under a law of force proportional to the distance.
(Newton proved this by other means.)

His next step was to consider motion in a circle in which the force
on the particle was not towards the centre of the circle but to some
other centre of force, S, say. The question then is, given S and C,
the centre of the circle, what law of force will enable the particle to

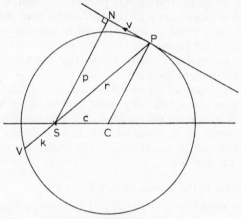

Figure 20

describe the circle? We can see how to do this by a little simple
geometry. If we draw the radius from the centre to the point P at
which the particle is (*Figure 20*) and suppose that the distance from
the centre of force S to the particle is r, while a perpendicular dropped
on to the velocity of the particle at the instant under consideration
is p, it is easy to see from Kepler's law that pv equals a constant
which is usually called h. For pv measures the rate of sweeping out
of sectorial area by the radius SP, as can be seen from *Figure 21*.
Here P, P' are two nearby points of the path, which are passed
through at times differing by the small amount t, so that $PP' = vt$,
and the area swept out in that short time is $\Delta SPP' = \frac{1}{2}pvt$. Now if
we ask for the required law of force F from P to S which is acting
to draw the particle inwards we have, of course, to know what is the
value of the acceleration of the particle. In particular the particle
will have accelerations both along and at right angles to the tangent
to the circle, and the one which we are most concerned with here is
the one along the radius at right angles to the tangent. It is generally

known that the acceleration along the inward radius of a particle moving in a circle of radius a is v^2/a where v is the velocity. In fact we can prove this very easily by imagining the distance that the particle goes in a short time t when the path is a circle; this distance

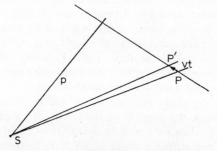

Figure 21

will be made up of a part PQ along the tangent and then a part QR at right angles to the tangent. If we complete the triangle SRN in *Figure 22*, so that NP is equal to RQ and NR and PQ are both vt, then we have at once by Pythagoras's theorem that SN^2 is $a^2 - (vt)^2$, so that we can write SN as $a\sqrt{1 - (vt/a)^2} \simeq a\left(1 - \dfrac{1}{2}\dfrac{v^2t^2}{a^2}\right)$. This

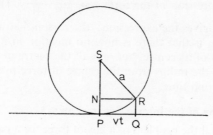

Figure 22

shows that for this short interval of time the distance gone at right angles to the tangent is $\dfrac{1}{2}\dfrac{v^2}{a}t^2$, and by comparing this with the expression for motion with a constant acceleration we see that the acceleration along the normal is v^2/a.

Looking then again at the particle moving in a circle with the centre of force S (*Figure 20*) and only considering the acceleration along the radius SP, we have at once by similar triangles that fp/r is equal to the part of the attractive force f, which is acting in the direction of the radius and this is mv^2/a; so the law of force which we require could be written in terms of v and r and p as $f = \dfrac{mv^2 r}{ap}$. However, this is not very convenient for several reasons. In the first place it involves the velocity, and we wish to know what the law of force is without having to determine the velocity first. However, we know that pv is constant, equal to h, and so we can replace the velocity and get the expression $mh^2 r/(ap^3)$. Since h is constant, we have an expression of the form r/p^3. However, this is still not particularly convenient because it involves both r and p and Newton converts it instead into an expression which brings in the point which lies on the other extreme of the radius from the centre of force to P, that is, the point V on the circle. If we call the distance from S to V, k, then we see at once that rk is equal to a constant. Moreover, if the distance from C to S is c, then we have, by Pythagoras's theorem, an expression for NP^2 in terms of p, that is $c^2 - (p - a)^2$. It follows that $c^2 - (p - a)^2 = r^2 - p^2$, and another way in which this can be put is that the distance SN, which is p, will be $[r^2 + a^2 - c^2]/2a$, which is equal to $\dfrac{r}{2a}\left[r + \dfrac{a^2 - c^2}{r}\right]$. The expression for the force which we had, that is $\dfrac{mh^2}{a}\left(\dfrac{r}{p}\right)^3 \dfrac{1}{r^2}$, is then the same as an expression of the form $f = \dfrac{K}{SP^2 . PV^3}$. This is the form which Newton gives the expression; the reason that he chooses this particular form is that there is now no mention in it of the radius of the circle or of its centre, but only of the centre of force, and the intersection of the radius from the centre of force to the point with the circle a second time.

Determination of the Inverse Square Law: 3

Having solved the problem of a law of force for a particle to move in a circle with any centre of force, Newton is then quite easily able to solve the problem of motion in a particular circle with two different centres of force. In *Figure 23* suppose that R and S are two centres of force, P being any particular position of the particle; PS cuts the circle again in V as before, and PR cuts the circle in U. We draw, through S, a line parallel to the other radius vector SG, then the law of force which is needed to describe the motion towards S is to that required to describe the motion under a force towards R as $\dfrac{RP^2 . PU^3}{SP^2 . PV^3}$. However, by considering the similar triangles PUV and SPG we see at once that the ratio SP/PU is SG/PV, and so the ratio

of the forces in question is that of $RP^2 . SP/SG^3$. Newton's geometrical ingenuity shows itself in the fact that this ratio now makes
no mention of the other points U and V on the circle, nor of the
centre or radius of the circle, but simply of the two centres of force

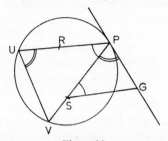

Figure 23

and the tangent to the curve. Newton was able to see at once that
this was of universal application, and not merely for application to
the circle alone. This was because he was arguing here about the
inward acceleration along the normal, that is, the line at right angles
to the tangent, and because this acceleration depended on the velocity
and the rate at which the curve was curving, or what we call the

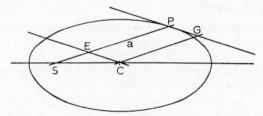

Figure 24

curvature of the curve. He was therefore able to apply it to the same
problem with an ellipse, one of the centres of force being the centre,
and the other being one focus. In *Figure 24* we now have the centre
C playing the part of one of the centres of force (S), and the focus S
as the other (R), and so we get the expression for f, by applying this
result that f towards the focus, f_R, is proportional to

$$CP \cdot \frac{CG^3}{SP^2 . CP} = \frac{PE^3}{SP^2},$$

where E is the point on the radius vector from the focus to the particle
at which it meets the line through the centre drawn parallel to the
tangent. It only remains to determine the length of PE for the ellipse,

and a little geometry shows this to be equal to the semi-major axis of the ellipse *a*. We may perhaps omit this last part* as having no great interest from the point of view of mechanics, and if we take it for granted that *PE* has the magnitude *a* then we have Newton's derivation of the inverse square law completed. Of course it does not follow from Kepler's law for one planet alone that the law of force must be an inverse square law, for the distance *SP* is given as being the distance to a point of the ellipse and so the law of force might have some dependence upon angle, which was of such a kind that for each point on the ellipse the part of the law of force which depended upon the angle was just such as to make the total force proportional to $1/r^2$ for that ellipse, but not for other points of space. However, when one has Kepler's laws for a number of planets, and all their orbits are ellipses, this way out is no longer open to us and we are forced to conclude that the sun attracts each of the planets with a force inversely proportional to the square of the distance. Then, if we do not wish to believe that the sun is a special body with properties different from other matter in the universe, we have to suppose that any two particles attract each other with a force proportional to the inverse square of the distance between them. And this is part of Newton's law of gravitation.

The Law of Gravitation

Our next step must be to use the remaining one of Kepler's laws, that the periodic times are proportional to $a^{\frac{3}{2}}$, where *a* is the semi-major axis. It is easy to find an expression for the periodic time, given *h*, the constant product of *p* and *v*, since we have already seen that $\frac{1}{2}h$ is the rate at which sectorial area is swept out, so that (because, as is obvious from *Figure 19*, the area of the ellipse is πab) the time taken to sweep out the whole area is $\dfrac{\pi ab}{\frac{1}{2}h}$.

Unfortunately *h* is not determined for us. However, at the ends of the major axis it is obvious from symmetry that the acceleration (towards *S*) is also along the normal to the ellipse, so that

$$\frac{mk}{r^2} = \frac{mv^2}{R},$$

where we write *mk* for the magnitude of the force at unit distance and *R* is the radius of the circle conforming most closely to the ellipse at the point considered.

To determine *R* we have again to imagine the orthogonal projection, which produces the ellipse, as having the same effect as

* See note at end of chapter.

drawing the original circle of radius a and reducing all the ordinates in *one* direction in the ratio b/a, leaving lengths in the perpendicular direction unchanged (*Figure 25*). From *Figure 25*, if the circle fits the ellipse as closely as possible at A, we have

$$DE = \sqrt{R^2 - (bh/a)^2} = \sqrt{a^2 - h^2} - (a - R),$$

when h is very small. Thus

$$R \left(1 - \frac{b^2 h^2}{2R^2 a^2}\right) \simeq a \left(1 - \frac{h^2}{2a^2}\right) - a + R,$$

which gives $R = b^2/a$.

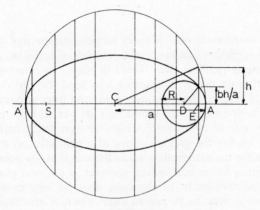

Figure 25

At the points A, A', then, we have

$$r^2 v^2 = kR = kb^2/a,$$

and $r^2 v^2$ *there* is, of course, h^2. Since, then, $h^2/k = b^2/a$, the periodic time is $\dfrac{2\pi}{\sqrt{k}} a^{3/2}$, and so Kepler's third law states that k is the same for each planet. Since k is the force per unit mass that the sun exerts on the planet this means that the force on any mass is proportional to that mass. But, from Newton's third law of motion, if we consider two masses attracting each other in turn in this way, the force must be proportional to each of them, that is, to their product.

If then an inertial observer sees any two particles of masses m, M moving under each other's gravitational attraction, but (he has some good reason for supposing) under no other influences he will infer that for one particle

$$mf = \frac{GmM}{r^2},$$

where f is the acceleration, which is towards the other particle at that instant, r is the distance between them, and G is a constant (the constant of gravitation) whose value in C.G.S. units turns out to be $6\cdot67 \times 10^{-8}$.

We may notice here that the fact that m occurs on both sides of the above equation allows us simply to specify the field due to M as an *acceleration field*

$$f = \frac{GM}{r^2}$$

which acts in the same way on every particle, irrespective of its mass. This fact is sometimes known as the *principle of equivalence* (because it really asserts that the two "kinds of mass" m entering into the equation, that on the left measuring how hard the particle must be pushed, and that on the right measuring the force produced in the particle by a given field, are equivalent). It was really a special case of the principle of equivalence which we were using earlier in the chapter in finding the greatest range of a projectile on an inclined plane, because the assumption made there is that, by going over to the description by an accelerated observer, a uniform gravitational field may be abolished. In the same way, so long as we confine ourselves to a very small region over which a gravitational field can be treated as uniform, the field can be abolished by an acceleration.

The environment now—with the gravitational field abolished—consists of descriptions by a number of accelerated observers. Such an environment is that used by the general theory of relativity, which was put forward by Einstein in 1915. It is the most satisfactory theory of gravitation which has been formulated up till now, but it is beyond the scope of the present book to describe the complex mathematics involved in it.

Instead, then, of incorporating the gravitational field in the environment, we shall adhere to the distinction between inertial and accelerated observers which has already been made clear in Newtonian mechanics.

To summarise our progress so far in disentangling the environment in mechanics, we can say that the Newtonian environment of an absolute (but unobservable) space has been replaced (without changing the observable structure of mechanics at all) by the set of all inertial observers, together with an absolute time-reckoning. This environment was first *consciously* formulated in the XIXth Century and achieved great successes in rationalising the basis of mechanics. In the next chapter we shall consider some unanswered problems raised by the process of determining the reference frames of the preferred inertial observers.

Note on the Geometry of the Ellipse

The result that $PE = a$ in *Figure 24* can be deduced easily from the "gardener's construction" of the ellipse. We have first to prove that the tangent at any point P makes equal angles with the focal distances PS, PH. Suppose (*Figure 26*) a nearby point Q is chosen

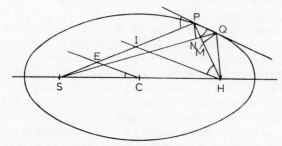

Figure 26

and draw PN perpendicular to SQ, and QM to PH. Then PQ is approximately the direction of the tangent at P (if Q is very near) and

$$SQ + QH = SN + NQ + PH - MP$$
$$= SP + PH + NQ - MP$$

so that
$$NQ = MP,$$

and therefore $\dfrac{NQ}{PQ} = \dfrac{MP}{PQ}$, which establishes the result.

Now since C bisects SH, E must bisect SI, so

$$PE = \tfrac{1}{2}(PI + PS) = \tfrac{1}{2}(PH + PS) = a,$$

since the angles marked are equal.

CHAPTER 3

MACH'S PRINCIPLE

Foucault's Pendulum

The position which we have now reached is that the environment for Newtonian mechanics consists of a set of preferred "inertial frames". However, the determination of these frames is not quite so straightforward in practice. In the first place the frames which are inertial are determined partly by a convention as to which particles are to be counted as under no forces. For example, near the surface of the earth the frames fixed to the earth are to a fair degree of approximation inertial if we allow that the particles are acted on by a gravitational force. If, however, we consider that a force only acts on a particle when it is constrained to move by means of a string, spring or some such connection, such a frame would not be inertial; but the frame considered in the last chapter which was falling freely so that a projectile move along a straight line would be inertial. Even if we allow for gravitational forces, the frames fixed to the earth are not exactly inertial, as we can see from the motion of a pendulum. If a very long pendulum (very long so as to show the effect more clearly) is started swinging in a vertical plane, (which can best be done by tieing the bob to one side by a piece of thread which is then burnt through by a match) it will be found that some hours later the pendulum is still swinging in a vertical plane, but not in the same one as before. The plane of swing of the pendulum rotates relative to the room in which it is fixed, and the usual way of explaining this at an elementary level is to say that the plane is not really rotating relative to the room but that the plane remains fixed and the room is being rotated because of the rotation of the earth. It is clear that this explanation assumes without saying so that there are preferred inertial frames with respect to which the rotation of the earth is measured. Such a pendulum experiment is really a measurement of the rotation of the earth relative to the environment of Newtonian mechanics.

Now there is another entirely different method of measuring the rotation of the earth. If we survey the sky with a telescope we can determine astronomically how the earth is moving relative to the general pattern of the stars. It is a remarkable fact that within the degree of accuracy of the observations these two methods of determining the rotation of the earth, although quite different in principle, give the same result. The first person to realise clearly the significance of this was Mach in 1893. Not everyone agrees with his view about the interpretation of these facts, but it is hard to see how *all* the facts can be explained otherwise than in Mach's way. It is impossible to believe that the frames of reference determined by local experiments should agree with those, with respect to which the distant stars are not rotating, simply by accident. There must therefore be some mechanism operating, which establishes the connection between the distant matter and the local inertial frames, that is the local environment. It is not feasible to suppose that the local environment is influencing the distant matter, and so we are forced to suppose that the distant matter influences the local environment. This is the statement known as Mach's Principle.

One of the most important consequences for us of this Principle is that the local environment defined by Newton's laws turns out to be intimately connected with the *actual* environment, that is the whole universe as we find it.

The Critical Nature of the Inverse Square Law

Before considering further consequences of Mach's Principle we may notice exactly how the most distant matter has a predominant effect. In this connection it is as well to consider the critical status of the inverse square law, shown by the following argument. Suppose that we can associate some numerical field with matter, determined by a law of force depending only on the distance, and suppose also, for the sake of simplicity, that the universe consists of a uniform distribution of matter. If we further assume that each particle of matter contributes equally to this effect, then three possible cases arise:

(*a*) If the law by which the field falls off with distance is one more rapid than the inverse square law then, since the amount of matter on a sphere with its centre on the earth and of radius r is proportional to r^2, the contribution from the matter on this sphere will be proportional to some negative power of r.

(*b*) In the same way, if the field falls off more slowly than the inverse square of the distance, the matter on a sphere of radius r will make a contribution proportional to some positive power of r.

(*c*) If the law is that of the inverse square, then the matter on a sphere of radius r makes a contribution which does not depend upon r at all.

Now in the first case the effect is a purely local one, the matter near to us having an altogether predominant effect. Such a situation cannot tell us anything about our environment in the sense of the universe. In the second case it is the most distant matter which has the predominating effect. This means that in principle a field of this kind can tell us about distant parts of the universe. Unfortunately, however, this is extremely difficult to observe in practice, since the large amount of very distant matter has an effect which altogether swamps any effect from matter in our locality which can be moved as we wish. It is therefore impossible to carry out any experiments with this field and its existence can only be inferred by rather subtle observations. The third case is rather like that met in gravitation, although there it is a force, having magnitude and direction, and not simply a number, which is in question. All the same, it is clear that the discovery of the inverse square law of gravitation was possible for Newton only because it was indeed the inverse square law which had to be discovered, and not some other power.

We have, of course, so far not explained any mechanism by which the connection between distant matter and local inertial frames described by Mach's principle could take place. However, if we tentatively assume that it is an effect not altogether unlike gravitation, with a law covering the way the effect falls off with distance, it is clear from the experimental results that this fall off with distance must be more slowly than the inverse square law. As a result the environment determined in this way would not vary appreciably as we go from place to place, and so, as far as our immediate locality is concerned, we would have something which is extremely like the absolute space which Newton wanted.

Einstein's discussion of Mach's Principle

The discussion of Mach's principle was taken up by Einstein in 1917. He argued that the existence of the inertia of matter, that is, the existence of a *mass* of a particle which measures the difficulty of moving it by means of a given force in Newton's second law, cannot be simply a property of the matter in space, but of the matter as it stands related to all the other matter in the universe. For the mass requires, for its determination, the existence of the local environment, and we have already seen that this local environment is determined by the distant matter. Einstein, assuming that the mechanism in Mach's principle would be one that decreased with distance, concluded that a particle which was sufficiently far removed from all other matter would have no mass. This conclusion would not, of course, follow if the mechanism in Mach's Principle were one which was independent of distance or even increased with distance. Proceeding with this argument Einstein imagined such a particle moving along in a completely empty universe. It will be completely undisturbed by inertia since its mass has vanished. Now let us imagine a speck of dust introduced into this otherwise empty universe.

This will, of course, cause a small change in the motion of the first particle. It is too much to try to believe that this speck of dust, however small, should restore the whole of the mass of the original particle since it is no longer in an empty universe. The effect of the speck of dust must be very small and so it can only lead to the first body acquiring a very small mass and so a small inertia. Arguing in this way Einstein was led to a quantitative form of Mach's Principle.

To see the full significance of this quantitative form we ought to recall how we distinguished between different concepts of mass in Newtonian mechanics which are initially confused. The mass which multiplies the velocity to produce the momentum and so is a measure of the inertia of the particle we shall call the inertial mass. The mass which occurs in the equation for Newton's law of gravitation (analogously to the occurrence of charges in the electro-static inverse square law) we shall call the gravitational mass. Einstein's form of Mach's Principle can now be expressed in the form: the inertial mass of any particle is determined by the gravitational masses of the rest of the universe and by their distribution. Now the gravitational effect of a particle is specified by its mass and by the constant of gravitation, and this mass is usually taken to be equal to the inertial mass of the particle. However, most people would agree that the gravitational mass of a particle is something which is determined only by the properties of the particle itself, so that, if Mach's Principle is correct, the ratio of these two quantities (which is measured by the constant of gravitation) tells us something about the whole universe. One consequence of this is that if at some time in the past the universe were in a state very different from its present one, then the constant of gravitation would have had quite a different value.

A number of people have raised objections to Mach's Principle, but these objections are usually misguided. It is often said that the Principle is a philosophical one rather than a scientific one, and so of no physical importance. This may be true of Mach's original way of looking at the Principle but it is certainly not true now. On the one hand we can deduce physical consequences from the truth of Mach's Principle; on the other it is not altogether hopeless to try to test its correctness experimentally. The universe looks much the same on average in every direction, but there are quite large local deviations from this, as we can see on any clear night by noting our own galaxy (the Milky Way). Such local deviations ought to show themselves in small differences of inertia in different directions. Some estimates of the size of the effect are that it may be something like one part in ten million, and this is quite near to what can be measured with present day apparatus.

Olbers' Paradox

Mach's Principle, if it is true, is an example of a long range effect. While we are considering such effects it is appropriate to consider another one, which also supplies us with information about the universe of a kind which is difficult to interpret. When we go out of doors on a clear night the most remarkable feature of our surroundings is the lack of radiation. The sky is completely dark except near each of the stars. We are used to this and so we do not question it, but the importance of this fact for the discussion of the universe as a whole was first pointed out by Olbers in 1826. He assumed that the average number of stars per unit volume and the average light from each star were constant everywhere and at all times, so long as the averages were taken over large enough regions. Such assumptions are very natural ones to make in order to simplify the discussion of such a complex system as the universe. The amount of radiation from the stars on a thin shell of radius r will now be proportional to the area of the shell, that is to r^2 and the light from these stars falls off in intensity according to the inverse square law, so that the amount contributed by this shell in our immediate locality is independent of r. If we imagine space divided up into a set of concentric shells then, since we can add the contributions from these shells without limit, it follows that the total radiation density in our locality, and therefore everywhere, is infinite. The result is extremely puzzling, but it is considerably altered by our realising that light from a star may not reach us because another star is in the way. It is easy to modify the argument to take account of this effect, and when we do this, instead of an infinite answer, we find that the local radiation density must be equal to the average at the surface of a star. This is very bright indeed, so we are still in the position that a straightforward argument from apparently obvious assumptions has led to a result quite at variance with experiment. Olbers found this result equally puzzling and he tried to explain it away by supposing that there was a very diffuse gas absorbing the radiation over long distances. However, such an explanation is hopeless for, if the gas absorbs the radiation, it must heat up until it reaches the temperature at which it radiates as much as it receives, and we are then back at the original paradox.

There are two obvious ways of dodging Olbers' paradox. We cannot, of course, assume that the average radiation density diminishes as we go away from this part of the universe in space, for this is a return to an idea of man as being at the centre of creation. We can, however, assume that the stars become less bright as we go backwards in time, and because the light takes a long time to reach us from the most distant matter, this means that this distant matter will in fact contribute less to the total than Olbers' calculation supposes. We can, in fact, make the answer agree with experiment by supposing that the stars did not radiate until something between a hundred million and a million million years ago. By astronomical standards we can summarise this answer to the problem by saying that it assumes that the universe is very young.

Another solution which is much more congenial to the astronomer is to observe that Olbers assumed that the matter was all, on an average, at rest. If we try to imagine how the matter should be moving to contribute a lower amount of radiation than Olbers' estimate, we must start by searching for some physical effect which will reduce the intensity of radiation. There is such an effect, the Doppler Shift, which we have already discussed in connection with sound waves in chapter 1. If the stars are receding from us the light of any particular frequency emitted from the star will appear reddened, that is, its frequency is lowered, since not so many wave lengths arrive in a given time. This means that the energy and therefore the intensity is reduced. Exactly how such a process can take place without putting man at the centre of creation needs further consideration, but if this can be done then it is possible to arrange that the recession of the distant matter will get us out of the trouble with Olbers' paradox. The second possibility then is that the universe is expanding. The surprising thing about such a conclusion, derived as it is from the very elementary observation that the night sky is dark, is that it appears to agree with the astronomical observations of distant matter, which was first found in the thirties to be receding from us with speeds proportional to its distance.

The Law of Recession

It will be as well here to consider how we can arrange the motions of matter so as to allow for the distant matter to recede and yet not have the earth in a privileged position at the centre of the universe. If we could not do this our theory would be no better than those which we have rejected earlier. It turns out that the assumption that the earth is not in a privileged position is able to give us a rather precise description of how the matter must move if it is not in fact to be at rest. Consider three particles of the universe. We can, if we like, take them as distant stars or indeed as galaxies, for within the vast considerations of present day cosmology, a galaxy is, in effect, equivalent to a point. Call these three A, B, and C and to simplify the argument, let us suppose that we have chosen three particles such that at the instant under consideration AB and AC are equal distances. We can imagine that everything lies in the plane of A, B

and *C*. Of course the real problem is a three-dimensional one, and this makes the analysis a little more difficult, but there is no real difference in principle and so we shall confine ourselves to the two-dimensional case in what follows. We then have everything happening in the plane of *A*, *B* and *C* and so the velocities of *B* and *C* relative to *A* can be worked out. If we take any two particles in the universe, and consider the velocity of the second one relative to the first, it is clear that this velocity can either be along the line joining

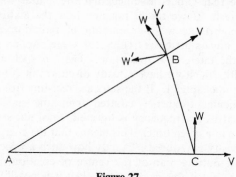

Figure 27

them or at right angles to it, or in general can have components in each of those directions. Moreover, these components cannot depend upon anything except the distance between the particles. For if they depended, for instance, on the angle which the line joining them makes with some fixed direction, then we would have this special fixed direction coming into consideration. But so far as we know all directions in the universe are equally good (that is to say, the universe is isotropic). And in the same way, if we start with one particle and look at the velocities surrounding it, and so derive the way in which the velocities depend on the distances from that particle, these same velocities would also be found starting with some other particle; otherwise the first one would be in a privileged position, and this we deny by saying that the universe is homogeneous. Let us then consider the expressions which we can find for the velocities of *B* in two different ways *Figure 27*. Firstly, by considering its velocity directly relative to *A*. There will then be some component of velocity, let us call it *V* along *AB*, and another component *W* at right angles to it, and here *V* and *W* depend only upon the distance *AB*. It follows at once from our assumption of isotropy and homogeneity that the velocities of *C* in the same way will be *V* along *AC* and *W* at right angles to it. These are both velocities of *B* and *C* relative to *A*, but of course the velocity of *B* relative to C will be of some magnitude, let us call it V' along CB and W' at right angles to CB, V' and W' being determined from BC in the same way as V and W are determined from AB. Thus the velocities of B relative to C in the two directions will simply be the result of compounding the velocities of B relative to A and those of C relative to A, except that these second velocities must be taken negatively. Now this composition of velocities can easily be carried out by the well-known triangle of velocities, because both of the components of the velocity of B relative to A must depend only on the length of AB and be either along AB or at right angles to it, and similar considerations apply to AC the lengths of these two being equal. It follows at once that the corresponding velocities along and at right angles to BC must be of a magnitude proportional to BC compared to the velocities for AB and AC, which would then have to be proportional to *their* lengths. This all follows because the triangle rule for compounding these velocities must hold. We therefore see that each of the particles can have two kinds of velocity, a velocity along the line joining it to the original particle and proportional to its distance, and a velocity at right angles to that line and also proportional to the distance. However, the second of these velocities can be disregarded for our purpose, for, since these velocities at right angles to the lines forming the triangle are all proportional to the distances between the particles, it follows that they are simply produced by a bodily rotation of the triangle as a whole with a suitable angular speed, and not by any change of size or shape in the triangle. We can therefore remove these velocities completely by suitably rotating our point of view keeping pace with the triangle. We are left with the radial velocities, that is with any two particles under consideration separating with a relative velocity proportional to the distance between them. This is obviously a perfectly possible situation in the plane, and it only requires a slightly more complicated analysis to show that it is possible in three dimensions as well. This then is the extremely precise picture of the expanding universe which arises as a result of Olber's paradox: any two particles of it separating by a velocity which is proportional to the distance between them. Such a velocity of recession is of course that actually found by the astronomers for the distant galaxies, and the law of increase of the velocity with distance is certainly close to one of being proportional to distance.

It is a most striking thing that a careful consideration of the very easily made observation of the dark night sky should lead in such a precise manner to a cosmological fact of great importance—the expansion of the universe. The reason why we are able to explain Olbers' paradox is because there is a well-understood physical effect—the Doppler shift—which can be called in to make good the discrepancy.

Let us return to the question of Mach's principle. If the local inertial frames are determined by something vaguely resembling a field of force, then this must fall off with distance more slowly than (or at the very least as slowly as) the inverse square. The total contribution of the most distant matter will then be infinite, in just the same way as the radiation in Olbers' calculation. There must be some information about the universe concealed here, if only we had the key (corresponding to Doppler shift for radiation) to unlock the door.

We have now come quite a long way in our analysis of the environment. The set of inertial observers which we reached in the last chapter, as a refinement of Newton's idea of absolute space, define an environment suitable for many dynamical experiments. If Mach's principle is to be believed, the corresponding inertial frames are determined by the distribution of matter in the actual universe, and the rather theoretical idea of environment is thereby intimately linked with the actual environment, in the most ordinary sense of the word.

We still have, however, the Newtonian absolute time. As soon as we pay proper attention to the way in which preferred inertial frames are set up, we find an immense enrichment of the concept of the environment, with many experimental consequences, which will be dealt with in the next two chapters.

CHAPTER 4

TRANSFORMATIONS BETWEEN INERTIAL FRAMES

Time Measurement for distant Events

In chapter 2 we mentioned that the question of time measurement in inertial frames was left on one side. We assumed with Newton that all observers would agree on a common measurement for the time of an event. From that restricted point of view it already followed in chapter 3 that the model of the universe which we were led to had to be an expanding one. This expansion certainly removes the difficulties of Olbers' paradox, and so it is conceivable that, if the mechanism of Mach's Principle is an appropriate one, it may also remove the corresponding paradox in which the rôle of the light in Olbers' paradox is played by the effect which determines the inertial frames.

Now we must leave these difficulties on one side as largely settled and return to the consideration of time measurement. The idea of a single universal time ordering of events is a very advanced one. We cannot appeal to observation to justify it directly, for there are many instances which appear to contradict it. For example, a distant observer sees a flash of lightning long before he hears the thunder, although a nearer observer can hardly detect any time interval. We can even witness a reversal of order when someone watches soldiers drilling from a distance and sees the men suddenly move before he hears the word of command which caused the movement. Of course, if we insist on our idea of a single time order, we can explain these apparent anomalies in terms of the speed of sound, but the point here is that the original idea is an abstraction from experiments, and one of a rather subtle kind. Einstein, in 1905, seems to have been the first person to realise that the idea of distant events being simultaneous with each other was something which needed careful consideration. He was able to show at that time that the only rules which one could give, for the determination of such simultaneity, gave criteria which were subjective, in the sense that different observers would form different conclusions about which events were simultaneous. This strikes at the very root of Newtonian mechanics and indeed of the whole concept of environment which has gone before in this book, though we may mention straight away that the errors involved are very small except when observers are moving relative to each other with very high velocities indeed.

The question of assigning times to distant events is tied up with the way in which one gets information about these events. It was known from very early times that sound travelled with a certain speed, for this was the cause of echoes. For a long time, however, light was thought to travel instantaneously (although Empedocles, 490–435 B.C., spoke of light as travelling and was criticised by Aristotle for it). In 1638 Galileo described an experiment which would suffice to determine the speed of light, if such a speed existed. He suggested that two persons equipped with lighted lanterns and a shutter should stand several miles apart and as soon as one sees the light of the other he uncovers his light. The speed of light, however, is so great that such an experiment stands very little chance of success, and in fact Galileo only tried it at a distance of less than a mile. The general principle behind Galileo's experiment was, however, the basis of the first experimental determination of the speed of light. The planet Jupiter has a number of satellites, and as a matter of fact the satellites were first observed by Galileo. In 1668 Cassini published tables of motion of these satellites which were recognised as fairly reliable, and the Danish astronomer Roemer studied the irregularities in the times of eclipse of these satellites in 1675. He was able to show that these irregularities were caused by the light from certain eclipses having to travel a greater distance to the earth than from others, because of the different position of the earth in its orbit round the sun. He calculated that the time required for light to traverse the earth's orbit was about 22 minutes; the correct value is about 17 minutes. The actual determination of the speed of light by Galileo's method was finally performed in the laboratory by Fizeau. In his experiment light passed between the teeth of a rotating tooth wheel, travelled several miles, and was then reflected back along the same path. The wheel was rotated at such a speed that the light reached the wheel again just when a tooth was in its way so that no light was received back. The velocity determined by this means, which is close to the latest determinations, is about 300,000 kilometres per second.

The Velocity of Light

A completely different development took place in 1873 when Clerk Maxwell published his electro-magnetic theory of light. He had formulated equations governing the electro-magnetic field, and had determined that these equations had solutions in the form of waves. In 1887 Hertz generated these waves in the laboratory, and of course they are now quite familiar to us in the form of radio waves. But Maxwell also noticed that light was an instance of such waves, though the frequency is much higher than the radio waves which we are accustomed to.

Einstein was of course familiar with Maxwell's theory and his actual starting point in 1905 was a very interesting one. He observed that there were solutions of Maxwell's equations corresponding to a wave moving with a certain velocity, which could be determined entirely by electro-magnetic means and which agreed closely with the measured velocity of light. Consider, he then said, what such a wave seems like to an observer moving along with it with the speed of light. This observer would see electric and magnetic waves of the same kind as Maxwell had already been able to determine for the wave solutions, with the exception that these fields were not moving along but were standing. No such solutions of Maxwell's equations exist, and from this puzzle Einstein was led at once to the idea that the speed of light is a rather particular quantity in physics whose status is quite different from that of the speed of sound. This fact was at once connected by him with the difficulty we have mentioned before of assigning times to distant events.

This assigning of time can only be done in terms of information which we receive about those events, and this information comes to us principally by means of light or other electro-magnetic radiations. It is true that we get a certain amount of information by means of sound or even by touching objects, but all these methods of deriving information convey it from place to place with a much smaller speed than that of light. Speaking from a practical point of view we know of no way of transmitting information more swiftly than that of light. This is not to say that higher velocities than that of light can never occur; for example, light itself moves in a medium whose refractive index is less than 1 with a speed greater than its speed in free space. But a careful analysis of the actual transmission of information in this case by a packet of waves shows that the information is still carried more slowly than the velocity of light in free space. Another way of looking at Einstein's rule is to suppose that an observer adopts some particular method for signalling as a means of deriving information about the time of distant events. If this observer knows the distance away of the event, and the speed of the signal, then, by observing the time of reception of the signal, he can calculate the time when the event occurred. But this velocity of the signal which is supposed to be known actually needs to be measured in terms of space and time and so we must already know how to measure time at distant places before we can measure the speed of the signal, and so assign times to these distant events. We are in a circle from which there is no escape except by some new assumption.

Einstein's Assumption

Einstein avoided this difficulty and at the same time answered his earlier problem about the electro-magnetic wave by assuming that the speed of light is a universal constant for all observers or at least for all observers at rest in inertial frames. Such a hypothesis was far beyond the experimental data available in 1905, but the truth of the matter is that Einstein was here defining a *convention* for measuring time at distant points. What one requires of a convention is not so much agreement with experiment, which is more or less automatic, but a general consistency. The question of whether he achieved this consistency is still sometimes regarded as open by a few people, but by far the greater majority believe that he did.

Einstein assumed then, without too much question, that in order to carry out this process (which has been called by Bridgman "spreading time through space") it was convenient and allowable to suppose that the velocity of light at all times and places was a universal constant, and to define the time of distant events by using this fact.

Now it does seem, when setting up a theory of this kind, that this assumption is quite unexceptionable, for the light obviously plays a unique role in being the fastest signal which we know how to send. Moreover it is well described by a particular theoretical set of equations, that is Maxwell's equations, which predict indeed, if properly understood, that it will have this universal character for its velocity. However, these arguments are not so strong as they need to be, in view of the rather paradoxical nature of the results of the theory and the extreme opposition which has been raised against it in various quarters ever since 1905 when it was first produced; indeed this opposition seems in certain quarters to be increasing rather than diminishing, although it is true to say that most physicists accept the theory. Instead, therefore, of supposing that the velocity of light is a constant and so serves us as a uniquely convenient way of spreading time through space, we shall take a more general point of view and follow the line of Whitrow which appears in his book published in 1961.* In Whitrow's treatment, instead of assuming anything about the velocity of light beforehand, we simply make a number of assumptions about the characteristics of signalling by means of light and establishing criteria for the time of distant events that way.

* G. J. Whitrow. *The Natural Philosophy of Time.*

Assigning Times and Distances

Consider the events consisting of an observer sending out a signal and having it reflected back from a distant event (*Figure 28*); let the event which consists of his sending the signal be E_1, say, let it be reflected back at the event E_2, and received by him again at the event E_3. We must first make an assumption corresponding to the fact that the signals sent by light are the fastest that we know of, so we begin by assuming:

Assumption 1 $t_3 > t_1$, unless, of course, E_2 is actually in the same place as E_1 and E_3, in which case $t_3 = t_1$.

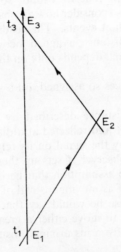

Figure 28

Further we suppose that the assignment of a time t_2 to the event is by a rule which determines t_2 uniquely, from t_1 and t_3. This is expressed by

Assumption 2 $t_2 = f(t_1, t_3)$.

Here the mathematical notation simply implies the existence of a rule by which, when t_1 and t_3 are given, t_2 is specified.

The problem, which we may call Einstein's problem, is to determine exactly what this rule is, or rather to formulate assumptions which limit this rule rather considerably. We have then to determine the rule which the observer may use to assign a time to the event E_2 when he knows t_1 and t_3. (We shall call the signals which are being employed here light signals, not because we are here assuming that they must be light, but because it is convenient to have a name for them, and in practice light or electromagnetic radiation is that usually employed for determining distant events in this way, for instance by radar.)

We now make two rather obvious assumptions about the behaviour of light:

Assumption 3 There is only one light path joining E_1 and E_2, and only one joining E_2 and E_3.

Assumption 4 (a) If 3 events E_1, E_2, E_3 occur in that order, along a light signal transmitted from E_1, then $t_3 > t_2$.

(b) If E_1, E_2, E_3 occur in that order along a light signal received at E_3, then $t_2 > t_1$.

It turns out, however, that we cannot solve Einstein's problem completely unless we also consider how an observer assigns distances, as well as times, to distant events. This leads to:

Assumption 5 The distance assigned between two events on a particular light-signal depends only on the times assigned to the events.

Assumption 6 Distances so assigned, on a straight line, add up in the usual way.

Assumption 7 The distance described by a light-signal emitted from an observer A and reflected at a distant event is the same as that described by the signal on its return journey to A.

In other words the observer A sets up these distances and times of distant events on the assumption that he is at rest.

If he regarded himself as moving instead of at rest, then he would reject this axiom because he would say that when the light beam returned to him, it had to move either a greater or a less distance, because he had moved from his original position.

The Assigning Function

We must now introduce a little mathematical symbolism. In the first place we already have a notation for the rule which assigns a time t_2 to a distant event which is observed by a light signal sent from the observer at time t_1 and reflected and received back again at time t_3. This relation was written in the form of $t_2 = f(t_1, t_3)$, this notation simply indicating that, when t_1 and t_3 are both given, t_2 is assigned. In the same way if t_1 and t_2 are the times which are theoretically assigned by A to two events on a light signal, we shall write for the distance apart which is assigned to them, the expression $g(t_1, t_2)$ where g now indicates simply that this distance is defined if, and only if, we know both the times t_1 and t_2. From our assumption about the addition law for distances we now have a rule of the form $g(t_1, t_2) + g(t_2, t_3) = g(t_1, t_3)$, or what would be more suggestively written as $g(t_1, t_2) = g(t_1, t_3) - g(t_2, t_3)$. In this form we see that, for any particular value of t_3 which does not occur on the left-hand side, the expression for $g(t_1, t_2)$ is given as the difference of two expressions, one of which does not involve t_2 and one which does not involve t_1, so that $g(t_1, t_2)$ is equal to some new expression, say, $h(t_1) - h(t_2)$.

Now let us use with this result the fact that the distance assigned to a distant event is the same in whichever direction the light is travelling, and suppose that the event E_2 is at a distance R away; then we have the expression $2R = h(t_3) - h(t_1)$, so that R is a half of $h(t_3) - h(t_1)$. In the same way we can see at once that $h(t_2)$ is a half of $h(t_3) + h(t_1)$, and this is actually an expression for the time assigned to E_2, for it comes to

$$t_2 = h^{-1} \left\{ \frac{h(t_3) + h(t_1)}{2} \right\},$$

h^{-1} being the inverse function of h, the argument of this function being the average of $h(t_3)$ and $h(t_1)$. The meaning of the inverse function is exactly the same as in various other parts of mathematics in which it occurs, for instance in trigonometry, that is the inverse function of h is the quantity which is such that h of it gives us the quantity under consideration. We know that such an inverse function will exist for the case of h because it is clear that $h(t)$ is something which increases when t increases. This is because h occurs in measuring the distance of events along a light path, and we shall suppose that if certain events are at increasing times along a light path, then they are also at increasing distances. When a function increases with its argument there is certainly an inverse function, as we can see at once by looking at a graph of the function. (*Figure 29*). Clearly everything about the assigning of both times and distances to a distant event depends upon this quantity $h(t)$ which we have introduced, and we have only to determine what sort of functions can enter as $h(t)$. The first thing that we notice from the expressions for t and R is that if we take a new function, say $H(t)$ of the form $ah(t) + b$, where a and b are constants, then a and b will fall out of the equations; that is to say, they will not really be involved at all, and so the same times and distances will be defined by $H(t)$ as by $h(t)$. The converse of this result is also true, that is to say, if we have two functions $H(t)$ and $h(t)$ which assign the same times and distances to distant events, then h and H will be related in this linear fashion. We can see this as follows. We have that

$$h^{-1} \left\{ \frac{h(t_1) + h(t_2)}{2} \right\} = H^{-1} \left\{ \frac{H(t_1) + H(t_2)}{2} \right\}$$

and so if we take a new function $F(t) = h\{H^{-1}(t)\}$, and take for our

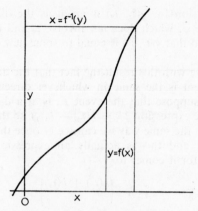

Figure 29(a) Existence of inverse function if $y = f(x)$ always increases (or always decreases).

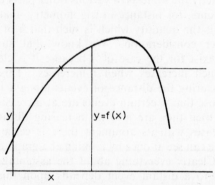

Figure 29(b) Non-existence of (unique) inverse function if $y = f(x)$ does not always increase or decrease.

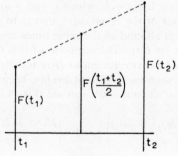

Figure 30

t_1 and t_2, $H^{-1}(x)$ and $H^{-1}(y)$, then we shall find that this new function F satisfies the equation, for any x and y, that F, of the average of x and y, is the average of $F(x)$ and $F(y)$. So long as F is a continuous function, that is to say, it has no breaks in its graph, which we should certainly assume for physical reasons in a case like this, it follows from this that $F(x)$ is a linear function of x, as we can see by drawing a graph of F between two points (*Figure 30*). This means that $hH^{-1}(t)$ is a linear function of t and so we can see at once that h is a linear function of H.

Whitrow's deduction of Einstein's Postulate

It is now appropriate to incorporate two further assumptions, which are certainly always made about time-keeping, although they are perhaps slightly less difficult to reject than the earlier ones.

Assumption 8 The time *interval* between two events assigned by an observer does not depend on how he sets the zero of his clock.

Assumption 9 If the unit of time-reckoning is changed for the measured times, it is changed in the same way for the assigned times.

Assumption 8 means that if t_1 and t_3 are both increased by an amount k, then t_2 must also be increased by an amount k, and so

whenever $\qquad h(t_2) = \tfrac{1}{2}\{h(t_1) + h(t_3)\}$,

then $\qquad h(t_2 + k) = \tfrac{1}{2}\{h(t_1 + k) + h(t_3 + k)\}$.

This is clearly an instance of the work which we have just done with the H and h; we simply choose for our $H(t)$, $h(t + k)$ and we therefore have from what we have just proved that $h(t + k)$ is some linear function of $H(t)$ which we can write as

$$h(t + k) = p(k)\, h(t) + q(k)$$

where $p(k)$, $q(k)$ take the place of the constants in the previous discussion. They will now, of course, depend upon the particular value of k which we have chosen. In particular, by choosing $t = 0$, we have

$$h(k) = p(k)\, h(0) + q(k),$$

and since we can without any loss of generality take $h(0) = 0$, for this simply corresponds to the change of zero of the time reckoning, it will then be clear that $q(k)$ is equal to $h(k)$. We therefore have the equation

$$h(t + k) = p(k)\, h(t) + h(k).$$

But, in this equation, t and k are simply any two numbers and we could therefore interchange them, that is to say write k for t and t for k, so that we also have

$$h(t + k) = h(k)\,p(t) + h(t).$$

By comparing these two results, it follows at once that

$$\frac{p(t) - 1}{h(t)} = \frac{p(k) - 1}{h(k)},$$

and since one side does not depend on t and one does not depend on k, both are constants, so that the function $p(t)$ is $1 + ah(t)$, where a is a constant. Two possibilities arise here; the constant a may be 0, or it may be non-zero. If the constant a is 0 then the function h has to satisfy

$$h(t + k) = h(k) + h(t),$$

and this equation, which is actually a well-known one, has only one solution so long as we are prepared to allow h only to be continuous and well-behaved in the manner to which we are accustomed for physical functions, (that is to say, the functions which occur in physics). This fact is obvious if we first consider $h(2t)$, which will be $2h(t)$, and then $h(3t)$, which will similarly be $3h(t)$, and so on. Proceeding in this way it is easy to show that, at least for any number x which can be expressed as the ratio of two integers, $h(xt)$ will be $xh(t)$. This will imply that $h(t)$ is actually proportional to t. The case in which a is non-zero is a little more complicated, but in fact we will not need to consider this, for it is not only the independence of the zero of clock-setting which we wish to incorporate into our devices. We also want to incorporate assumption 9 so that if, for instance, the numbers assigned to t_1 and t_3 are doubled then also the number assigned to the time t_2 by the observer is doubled. This will be found to require that the constant a actually is zero. For if a is not 0, then we can easily deduce something about the way the function p must depend upon t and k. If a is not 0, we can see by comparing $h(t + (k + t))$ and $h(2t + k)$ that

$$p(t + k) = p(t)\,p(k),$$

from which it follows that $1 + ah(t + k)$ is given by

$$1 + ah(t + k) = [1 + ah(t)]\,[1 + ah(k)],$$

Thus h must satisfy this "functional equation". On the other hand if the change of the time unit is not to make any difference, then in particular it will not make any difference if we halve the unit of time and so replace $h(t)$ by $h(2t)$ everywhere. Now $h(2t)$ from the original definition of $h(t + k)$ is $[1 + p(t)]h(t)$, and if we use the fact that

$h(2t_2)$ must be the average of $h(2t_1)$ and $h(2t_3)$ we see at once that $p(t_2)$, $p(t_1)$ and $p(t_3)$ must all be equal. But this equality is for arbitrary values of t_1 and t_3 and therefore $p(t)$ must be a constant. In other words, the equation which we have down to be satisfied by $p(t + k)$ as a product of $p(t)$ and $p(k)$ has to be satisfied by this constant value of p and therefore p must be either 1 or 0. Now p cannot be 0 because in that case $h(t + k)$ would be the same as $h(t)$, and this would lead up to no sensible determination of time at all, but simply to a trivial situation. Therefore p must be 1 and $a = 0$, so that we are back in the previous case where $h(t)$ was proportional to t. From the way in which h was introduced, then, the time assigned to a distant event which is illuminated by a signal leaving the observer at time t_1 and returning at time t_3 is $\frac{1}{2}(t_1 + t_3)$. This was the assumption made by Einstein and sometimes called Einstein's postulate, but we see here how this postulate is really unavoidable if we make the rather obvious assumptions we have made about time-ordering and independence of zeros and units.

We have really no choice but to assign the time to distant events in this way. It is not an experimental fact but something which is already determined by the way in which we speak of times and distances. It also follows that the distance of the event, R, is $\frac{1}{2}(t_3 - t_1)$, apart from a constant multiplier, so that the observer necessarily has to assign to events a distance proportional to the difference of time that it takes a signal to go and return. This is equivalent to his assuming a constant velocity of light, which as we said before was exactly what Einstein did. We see that the constancy of the velocity of light is not so much an experimental assumption as a necessary consequence of the way that we think about times and distances. Of course, people did not always analyse the way in which they thought about times and distances in this way, because the idea that the velocity of light was a constant was a difficult one to reconcile with their normal ideas of velocity which they had derived by thinking about billiard balls or horses, or whatever mechanical devices they may have used to get their ideas of velocity from. The velocity of light must be a speed in rather a different sense from the speed of a cricket ball, for otherwise it would not have this peculiarly constant nature. Nonetheless we are forced to assign to it this constant nature, even if it does mean a revision in our ideas of velocity, if we wish to retain our ideas of how one should assign times and distances to distant events.

The Background of Inertial Frames

Let us summarise the situation which we have reached in our discussion of the background implied by Newtonian Mechanics and by refinements of Newtonian Mechanics. Newton started with the idea of absolute space mainly because this was a philosophical necessity for him. He realised quite well, and it was the cause of much embarrassment to him, that his equations did not single out this absolute space for him; they only singled out a whole set of observers who would observe his first and second laws of motion to be true. Those are what we have called the inertial observers, any two of these observers moving uniformly relative to each other. In all of that description of the background, that is the set of inertial observers, we have adopted Newton's assumption that there is an absolute time variable, the same for all observers, which can be assigned to an event, no matter where the event is happening. In this way we can determine whenever two events occur at the same time, and so we finish that part of our discussion with the idea that the background was a set of all inertial observers with a common time-reckoning. We have now gone a little further and analysed this assumption of the common time-reckoning, and we now find that the set of all inertial observers can only be an approximation to the truth, because the different observers must allot times to distant events according to certain rules, and we have as yet no assurance of how these rules will agree with each other, if indeed they will agree. Our background now is still the set of inertial observers, but we have at the moment the problem still uninvestigated of how their measurements will be related to each other, in particular, how their time measurements will be related to each other. We can confidently expect that their measurements of spatial distances will be related in very much the same way as Newton's observers related their spatial measurements; that is to say, if two observers are moving with speed v one relative to the other, then the distance which one of them measures as x the other will measure as roughly $x - vt$. This statement is exactly true for Newton and it must be at least very approximately true still when we take account of the way in which time is spread through space. But whether the times assigned to a distant event by the two observers would be the same or not is something which will need investigation in the next chapter. The refinement of the environment which results from this investigation leads to many predictions of experimental results, which previously would have been mysterious.

CHAPTER 5

MEASUREMENTS BY TWO OBSERVERS

The Relative Speed of Two Observers

We have now established that an observer who wishes to spread time through space, that is, to assign a time to events which are distant from him, must do so in a way which makes the velocity of light a constant. To be more precise, he must do this if he wishes his assignment of times and distances to the distant events to satisfy the assumptions which we gave in the last chapter. But these assumptions are of such a straightforward and evident kind that it would be a brave man indeed who tried to formulate a theory in which they did not hold. Since then we are to have a constant value for the speed of light, it will be much more convenient in what follows to adopt only one fundamental unit, say that of time, and to define lengths in terms of this unit. That is, we adopt one second as the unit of time and the distance that light could travel in one second as the unit of distance (about 186,000 miles). In these units the speed of light will then always be 1, so that its constancy is incorporated from the very beginning.

Let us now see how two observers O, O' in motion relative to each other will assign times and distances to a distant event. It is convenient to look at everything from the point of one of these observers O, and the diagram for his motion will then be a straight line along the time axis simply representing the passage of time as measured by him (*Figure 31*). The observer, O, can now determine the relative motion of the observer O'. It is convenient to take the zero of both observer's time reckonings as their instant of coincidence. O sends a signal at time t_1 which is received and reflected by the second observer at time t_2' and returns to the first one at time t_3. We know that the first observer determines the distance of the second one as $x_2 = \frac{1}{2}(t_3 - t_1)$, and he also assigns to the time of reflection the value $t_2 = \frac{1}{2}(t_3 + t_1)$. Now the time at which the second observer receives the signal from the first, t_2', depends only on their relative motion and the time when the signal was sent. If O sends the signal at time $2t_1$, these times being measured from the instant at which the two observers were coincident, it is clear that, if the curve representing the second observer is a straight line, he will receive the signal from O at time $2t_2'$. In general the ratio of t_2' to t_1 is a certain constant which is determined by the speed with which the observers are separating. We shall call this constant k and we then have the relation $t_2' = kt_1$. Since the velocity of light is constant for all observers, it follows in exactly the same way that the ratio t_3/t_2' of the times of reception and transmission of the returning signal is also constant, depending only on the velocity of separation of the two observers and therefore having the same value as the

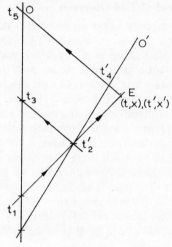

Figure 31

previous ratio. We can therefore express the time and distance of the event (as assigned by O) which is the reflection of the light at the second observer, in terms of t_1, in the following form

$$t_2 = \tfrac{1}{2}(k^2 + 1)t_1, \; x_2 = \tfrac{1}{2}(k^2 - 1)t_1.$$

If we divide the distance by the time we get an expression for the velocity v with which the observers are separating and so we have

$$v = \frac{k^2 - 1}{k^2 + 1}.$$

We notice that v is certainly less than 1, so that the constant velocity introduced by the axioms of the last chapter is also a *maximum* velocity of separation of observers. The constant k is the one which is most convenient to use in what follows to specify the relation between the observers, but for historical reasons we shall also translate the results into the corresponding ones in terms of the speed of separation because this is how they are most usually quoted.

The Einstein Velocity Formula

Let us now go on and compare the times and distances assigned to some other event by the two observers. We can imagine that the event E is one which is illuminated by a signal from the first observer at time t_1 and therefore from the second observer at time t_2' and we can suppose that the reflected light from the event reaches the two observers at times t_4', t_5. We then have the relations

$$t_2' = kt_1, \qquad t_5 = kt_4',$$
$$t = \tfrac{1}{2}(t_1 + t_5), \qquad x = \tfrac{1}{2}(t_5 - t_1),$$
$$t' = \tfrac{1}{2}(t_2' + t_4'), \qquad x' = \tfrac{1}{2}(t_4' - t_2'),$$

and the results of these can most conveniently be written in the form

$$t' + x' = \frac{1}{k}(t + x), \qquad t' - x' = k(t - x).$$

However these results are usually expressed in the following form, which is the well-known Lorentz Transformation:

$$t' = \frac{1}{2}\left(k + \frac{1}{k}\right)(t - vx), \qquad x' = \frac{1}{2}\left(k + \frac{1}{k}\right)(x - vt).$$

We shall now consider some simple consequences of these methods of assigning times and distances to distant events. In the first place let us imagine that there are three observers instead of two, and let us call them O, O_1, O_2. If k_1 is the constant which occurs in transforming the formulae of O into those of O_1 and k_2 is the constant which transforms O_1's measurements into O_2's, then from the form of the transformation it is at once obvious that the constant which transforms O's measurements directly into O_2's will be $k_1 k_2$. It is useful to express this result in terms of the velocities of the observers; if we regard O as at rest and suppose that O_1 is moving with a velocity v_1 and O_2 with a velocity v_2 relative to O_1 we have, for the velocity V of O_2 relative to O the fact that it corresponds to $k_1 k_2$ which is

$$\sqrt{\frac{1 + v_1}{1 - v_1}} \sqrt{\frac{1 + v_2}{1 - v_2}}.$$

From this we can derive the expression

$$V = \frac{v_1 + v_2}{1 + v_1 v_2}.$$

3

For the resultant of two velocities v_1 and v_2 in Newtonian Mechanics the corresponding expression would be simply the numerator of this. The denominator differs from 1 by a term which is a product of the two velocities but, of course, since we have made the speed of light unity, this product will be very small for all the speeds which we are accustomed to in everyday life. If we want to use the original units for space and time we should have to divide the product of velocities in the denominator by the square of the speed of light so that for most terrestrial applications the denominator is effectively unity. It is therefore not surprising that Newton was led into no trouble by supposing that he could unambiguously assign a time to distant events, and so use the sum of two velocities as their resultant. The present formula (the so-called Einstein velocity formula) has some very direct applications. We mentioned in chapter 1 the experiment of Fresnel in which light is passed through a stream of water moving with speed v and is found to have a velocity intermediate between c/n, which it would have if the water were at rest, and $c/n + v$ which it would have if it were carried along by the water. If we consider Fresnel's experiment according to an observer who is moving with the water the velocity of light will be c/n according to this observer. When we transfer to an observer fixed relative to the source of the light, we shall have to combine with this speed the speed of the water and so we get the expression

$$\frac{c/n + v}{1 + \dfrac{cv}{nc^2}},$$

which is to a sufficient approximation

$$\frac{c}{n} + v \left(1 - \frac{1}{n^2}\right),$$

the result found experimentally by Fresnel. Although this experiment is less accurate than some of those used to test the special theory of relativity it has the great advantage of being very direct and simple, and it is, of course, particularly valuable to us because of its being readily expressed in terms of the interaction of a system and its environment.

Distant Simultaneity

We have remarked that Newton was at fault in supposing that he could unambiguously assign a time to distant events. This means that, if two events not in the same place are simultaneous according to one observer, they will not be simultaneous according to another. It is instructive to work out the amount of the difference between the times of the events according to a moving observer. In *Figure 32* we can imagine two events to which a signal is sent by the observer

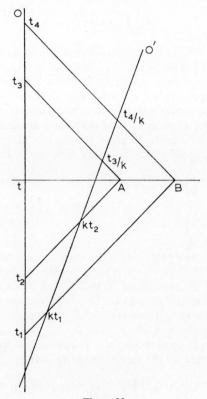

Figure 32

O at times t_1 and t_2 and these signals are received back at times t_4 and t_3 so that the observer sees both the events as occurring at the same time t. If a second observer sees the light signals passing him at kt_1, kt_2 on their outward journey, and at t_4/k, t_3/k on their inward journey, then we have the following relations between the various times assigned:

$$t_A = t_B = \tfrac{1}{2}(t_1 + t_4) = \tfrac{1}{2}(t_2 + t_3),$$

$$t_A' = \tfrac{1}{2}(kt_2 + t_3/k), \qquad t_B' = \tfrac{1}{2}(kt_1 + t_4/k).$$

The difference between the times assigned to the two events by the second observer is therefore

$$t_A' - t_B' = \frac{1}{2}\left[k(t_2 - t_1) + \frac{1}{k}(t_3 - t_4)\right]$$

$$= \frac{1}{2}\left(k - \frac{1}{k}\right)(t_2 - t_1),$$

which is never zero unless t_2 and t_1 are equal, in which case the two events are at the same point. It is instructive to pursue this a little further. Instead of dealing with the formulae in terms of the constant k, we may suppose that we are using the conventional Lorentz formulation and suppose that we have two events at distances x_1 and x_2 from an observer, which are at the same time t, according to this observer. The two times for these events, according to an observer moving with a speed v relative to the first, are

$$t_1 = \frac{1}{2}\left(k + \frac{1}{k}\right)(t - vx_1),$$

$$t_1 - t_2 = \frac{1}{2}\left(k + \frac{1}{k}\right)v(x_2 - x_1),$$

$$t_2 = \frac{1}{2}\left(k + \frac{1}{k}\right)(t - vx_2),$$

so that the second observer sees the events in a time order which is determined by their position. This suggests that two observers may disagree about the time order of two events, when neither of them sees the events as simultaneous. This is indeed the case, as we can see by using the same formulae and supposing that the two events are labelled by the first observer as (t_1, x_1), (t_2, x_2), where we can suppose that t_2 is greater than t_1. The corresponding difference of times as measured by the second observer is then

$$\frac{1}{2}\left(k + \frac{1}{k}\right)[t_2 - t_1 - v(x_2 - x_1)]$$

and is therefore positive or negative according as

$$t_2 - t_1 \gtrless v(x_2 - x_1).$$

Now v must be less than 1, so that the diagram on which we lay out the events observed by O is divided up into four parts by this relation. So long as the difference of the x's is less than the difference of the t's, that is, so long as a signal could pass between the two events with speed less than or equal to that of light, any two observers agree about the time orders of the events. If the difference of the x's is greater than the difference of the t's, so that the events can not be connected by a signal, unless it were one which moved faster than light, the event which one observer considers the earlier will be considered by some others as the later. The signals through the earlier event, according to O, then divide the plane up into the four parts mentioned, but it is only the events which are earlier or later than E, and fall in those parts which contain the time axis, which are placed in the same time order by any observer. If an event is separated from the time axis by one of these signals, there always exists an observer who will place this event in the opposite time order relative to that of E from the order assigned by O (*Figure 33*).

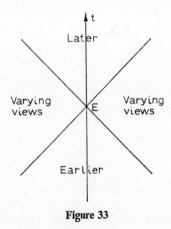

Figure 33

Another way of seeing this is shown in *Figure 34*. Let us enquire what events (described by O's measurements) are assigned equal times by an observer O'. From *Figure 32* the time assigned to an event by O' is

$$t' = \tfrac{1}{2}(kt_1 + t_4/k),$$

where O assigns

$$t = \tfrac{1}{2}(t_1 + t_4), \qquad x = \tfrac{1}{2}(t_4 - t_1).$$

Since

$$t_1 = t - x, \qquad t_4 = t + x,$$

we have

$$t' = \frac{1}{2}\left[\left(k + \frac{1}{k}\right)t - \left(k - \frac{1}{k}\right)x\right]$$

$$= \left(k + \frac{1}{k}\right)\left[t - \frac{k^2 - 1}{k^2 + 1}x\right],$$

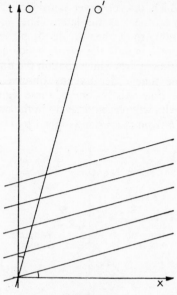

Figure 34

so that all events for which t' is constant have $t - vx$ constant. These sets of events are represented by a series of parallel lines (*Figure 34*), and since $x/t = 1/v$ these lines are inclined to the x-direction at the same angle as O''s path is to the t-direction.

As O''s speed is taken to be larger, the parallel set of equal-time lines assumes a position nearer to O''s path. In the limiting case when O''s speed is almost 1 the situation in *Figure 35* obtains.

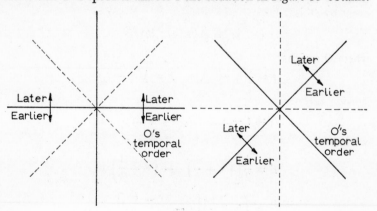

Figure 35

The Stretching of Measured Time

As well as the difference of time ordering, the formulae we have been considering also show a difference in the magnitude of the times assigned by the observers to events. For instance, starting with the Lorentz formulae, if we consider a set of events such as the ticks of a clock, which is at rest relative to the observer O at a point which he determines as distant x from him, the ticks being at t_1, $2t_1$, $3t_1$, . . . etc., then the corresponding times measured by an observer O' are given by $\beta(t_1 - vx)$, $\beta(2t_1 - vx)$, $\beta(3t_1 - vx)$, . . . where we now write β for the factor $\frac{1}{2}(k + 1/k) = (1 - v^2)^{-\frac{1}{2}}$, so that the interval between the ticks as measured by O' is seen to be βt_1, which is longer than the interval which the clock is supposed to register, and therefore O' considers the clock to be going slow relative to his own clock. This is often put in the rather confusing form "moving clocks go slow". This form is confusing because it seems paradoxical; each of the observers is moving relative to the other and it cannot be the case that each of the clocks is going slow although it is the case that each of the observers assigns a rate to the other clock as going slow relative to his own. The fact that this argument works both ways is a simple consequence of the Lorentz equations, for if we consider the clock at rest relative to the observer O' we have in exactly the same way $\beta(t_1 + vx)$, $\beta(2t_1 + vx)$, ... However there is only the appearance of paradox here, for the observers can only assign time to distant events by a rule, and in this present experiment the two observers can never again be in the same place, to compare their clocks and see whether one of them is correct or not in supposing that the other's clock is slow. It is otherwise with a more detailed experiment, known as the clock paradox, which was noticed by Einstein himself when formulating the theory in 1905. This paradox is quoted nowadays in a number of different forms, not all of them equivalent, and the rather subtle differences between these forms have led to a great deal of argument.

For the present we will consider the following form in which the edge of paradox is slightly blunted but the form has the advantage of being completely describable in terms of what we have done already. Suppose that an observer O is at rest, as we have considered before, and at time $t = 0$ on his clock an observer O' passes him with a speed v. O' moves off to a great distance and while he does so O sends signals to him and receives back reflections. At a great distance O' has the good fortune to meet another observer O'' who is moving towards O with exactly the same speed as O' is moving away. At the moment when they are coincident these two observers check their time reckonings against each other and O'' then returns and passes O again as shown in *Figure 36*. The event of the meeting of O' and O'' is duly observed by O who has sent out a signal to it at time t_1 so that O' observes the time to be kt_1 and therefore O'' assigns the total time for the journey as $2kt_1$. The light signal from the meeting of the astronauts returns to O at time $t_2 = k^2 t_1$ and from the symmetry of the figure it is obvious that O assigns the time

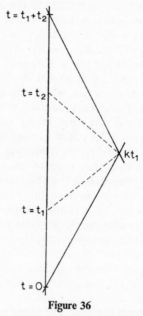

Figure 36

$t_1 + t_2$ to the journey. Now $1 + k^2$ is always greater than $2k$ as can be seen from the fact that

$$1 + k^2 - 2k = (1 - k)^2 > 0.$$

Let us suppose that this experiment is a valid idealisation of the experiment in which the observer O' leaves the observer O with a certain velocity, and at a great distance away turns rather sharply and comes back with the same velocity. This second experiment is obviously not identical with the first, since only two observers are concerned, but we are not at this point able to describe the way in which the observer turns round, since he must accelerate in order to do this and the consideration of accelerated observers comes later in this chapter. However, if the acceleration happens very quickly it is likely that the direct effect of the acceleration will be very small compared with its indirect effect in producing a change of speed, and therefore the original experiment gives us a close approximation of what happens in the second experiment. If this is so then the observer who has stayed at home will find that he is older than one who has been on the journey. This prediction is a surprising one, but it does *not* conflict with our experience since we have no experience of such long journeys at the high speeds necessary to show the effect.

At the same time it leads to surprising results if we suppose that we can include biological systems among those things affected by the consequences of this theory. For example if we imagine two caterpillars, one of them at rest with the observer, and the other moving off and returning, it is imaginable (according to the theory) that the stay-at-home caterpillar would be a butterfly when the returning wanderer was still only a caterpillar. The reason that this is called a paradox is because some people wrongly imagine that Einstein made some statement to the effect that all motion was relative and that therefore the two observers O and O' were equally entitled to their descriptions of the events. If this were so, then each caterpillar would have both to be a butterfly and to consider that the other must still be a caterpillar. It is obvious that there is no such symmetry between the two observers. One of the observers has remained at rest, the other had, at the extreme end of his journey, to undergo a violent acceleration. It is true that we neglect the direct effect of this acceleration on his clock, but its indirect effect is clear. Since only one of the observers has accelerated, it follows that their descriptions of the events are not equivalent and it is therefore not in the least paradoxical that one finds the other to be older, although it is of course a surprising and interesting consequence of the theory.

Since the clock paradox has given rise to so much argument, we shall give a discussion of accelerated observers later in this chapter, though the intrinsic importance of this is not so very great.

To prevent confusion, it may be as well to mention that the clock paradox is often formulated in a different way in which there is symmetry between the observers; for example, both observers might move relative to an inertial frame and then return again. In that case they will both agree on the time when they return but this does not affect the result in the case which we have considered. Whether the measured time described here agrees with the time experienced by ageing of living creatures is perhaps open to question, but there is very direct evidence for the change in time reckoning with motion in cosmic ray physics. At the earth's surface the meson showers observed have a soft component consisting of μ-mesons. These are charged particles about 207 times as heavy as the electron. In the laboratory such particles are found to have a life time of about two millionth's of a second, at the end of which time they decay into an electron and two neutrinos. It is known that these mesons are produced mainly in the upper atmosphere, about 10 kilometres up, by high energy collisions, and they then travel towards the earth with speeds very near to that of light. On Newton's ideas of time, even if the particles travel with the speed of light they can only travel about 600 metres before they decay, and they would therefore never be observed on the earth's surface. However, the life-time quoted above is that for an observer at rest relative to the meson. If we consider an observer at rest on the earth's surface, with respect to whom the mesons are moving very rapidly, the meson's "clock" will be going slow by a factor of at least 10, and the mesons can therefore travel at least 6 kilometres. The faster ones will have an even longer life time and so can easily reach sea level.

Observers moving with Constant Acceleration

It will be easy to discuss the clock paradox in a more realistic way if we consider how to describe acceleration, while paying attention to the lack of a common time measurement of different observers. In particular, let us try to formulate the idea of a constant acceleration in such a way that two observers in uniform motion will agree that the acceleration is constant. The more obvious ways of doing this lead to difficulties, because what one observer sees as a constant acceleration the other sees as a changing one. In such a situation the most sensible thing to do is to try to look at the problem from the point of view of some particularly appropriate observer, and then to make the whole thing unchanged when we go from one observer to another. This process sounds a little complicated, but it will be made clear if we actually carry it out. When we are considering the acceleration of a particle, it is clear that the speed is of no importance. There is, therefore, at each instant a particular observer, who is singled out from the others by the fact that he is at rest relative to the particle. Not only is this observer unique, he is also the observer with respect to whom the particle for a short time is moving with a very small speed, and when the speed is very small we know that Newtonian mechanics is a very good approximation. Our programme then is to make the value of the acceleration measured by the rest-observer a constant. Suppose the speed at any time is v and a short time later is $v + h$. If we transfer to the observer who at the beginning of the period is moving with the particle with the constant speed v the corresponding values of the velocities are given by the Einstein velocity formula as zero and

$$v' = \frac{v + h - v}{1 - v(v + h)} \simeq \frac{h}{1 - v^2} = \beta^2 h.$$

The difference in velocities at the beginning and end of the period is therefore less according to this observer and has the value $\beta^2 h$. The corresponding time measurements for the two observers can now be found by the Lorentz formula. We have

$$t = \beta t', \qquad t_1 = \beta t_1' \qquad \text{(say)}$$

so that if we take the particle instantaneously at rest according to O', we shall have the difference of times

$$t_1' - t' = \frac{1}{\beta}(t_1 - t).$$

The difference of velocities divided by the difference of times comes to

$$\beta^3 \frac{h}{t_1 - t} = \beta^3 f$$

where f is the Newtonian acceleration, and this is the quantity which has to be a constant for motion under constant acceleration. We can call this quantity the relativistic acceleration and we notice that when it is constant the Newtonian acceleration f is always less than the acceleration which the particle would have according to Newtonian mechanics, falling to zero when the speed gets near to that of light. We can now determine how the speed changes in motion with constant relativistic acceleration. To do this we have to express the relativistic acceleration in a slightly different form. For this purpose let us calculate the value of the form βv, which occurs in the Lorentz formula, when the velocity is increased by a small amount h. We have by a little algebra

$$\frac{1}{\sqrt{1 - (v + h)^2}} \simeq \frac{1}{\sqrt{1 - v^2}} + \frac{hv}{(1 - v^2)^{3/2}}$$

so that the difference

$$\beta'(v + h) - \beta v = (\beta + \beta^3 h v)(v + h) - \beta v$$
$$\simeq (\beta + \beta^3 v^2)h = \beta^3 h.$$

As a result we can express the constancy of the relativistic acceleration by saying that the quantity βv has a constant rate of change, just as in Newtonian Mechanics the speed has a constant rate of change for a constant acceleration. This means that the speed for constant relativistic acceleration g is determined by the formula

$$\beta v = gt,$$

so that at time t we have for the speed

$$v = \frac{gt}{\sqrt{1 + (gt)^2}}.$$

There is an immediate application of this formula in Newton's second law. Newtonian Mechanics is, of course, formulated, as we have seen, by assuming an absolute time for all observers. We cannot carry it over immediately when we are being more careful, and considering the determination of times by light signals. However, we do know that Newtonian Mechanics works very well for very slow speeds, and so it is natural to assume that it is exactly true for the observer with respect to whom a particle is instantaneously at rest. This observer will say that the force on the particle is measured by its mass times its acceleration, and it follows that an observer with respect to whom the particle is moving with a speed v will find a force measured by the product of the mass and the relativistic acceleration. Now its relativistic acceleration, as we have seen, is the rate of change of

$$\beta v = \frac{v}{\sqrt{1 - v^2}},$$

whereas the Newtonian acceleration is the rate of change of the speed. Newton's formula for mass, in terms of rate of change of momentum, can be taken over completely if we agree to reckoning the momentum of a particle moving with speed v as

$$\frac{mv}{\sqrt{1 - v^2}},$$

We have now progressed considerably in our analysis of the environment. If the environment is the set of inertial frames, corresponding to uniformly moving observers, with transformations of the form we have found, we are forced to alter our definition of momentum, not to mention the need to admit differences in elapsed time for observers who separate and regain each other. In the rest of this chapter we shall work out a few of the many consequences of this new environment, choosing some of intrinsic importance and some with results which we need in the later chapters.

The Increase of Mass with Velocity

The easiest way of interpreting the increase of momentum above the Newtonian level for a given speed is to say that the mass increases, since masses are in fact determined by means of the momentum or the rate of change of momentum of particles. The formula for the increase of mass is (writing m_0 for the rest-mass)

$$m = \frac{m_0}{\sqrt{1 - v^2}},$$

and as a matter of fact an increase of mass with velocity had already been found before special relativity by Kaufmann, in 1901, in experiments designed to determine the charge-mass-ratio for fast electrons emitted by radium. If we expand this expression for mass in terms of velocity we have, as far as the second order in the speed, two terms, one of which is obviously recognisable as the kinetic energy of the particle in Newtonian Mechanics, and the other consists simply of the mass, or, as we must now call it, to distinguish it from the measured mass at a certain speed, the rest-mass. From the fact that the kinetic energy is added to the rest-mass at least for values of the velocity for which this approximation holds, Einstein was led to see the rest-mass of the particle as representing a *rest energy* which could perhaps be released in some way. It is probably not too much to say that the resulting relation

$$E = mc^2$$

(where we have inserted the speed of light so that we may use the original units) is the most important consequence of relativity theory to-day, if only because of its political implications. From this relation we can make predictions about nuclear reactions, if we also assume that the total energy remains unchanged, an assumption which is amply justified in other fields. One consequence is that the mass of a stable nucleus must be less than the sum of the masses of its consituents, the difference being the energy which holds the parts together. This difference is therefore the energy which will be sufficient to disintegrate the nucleus.

To take an instance, the atomic mass of $_3Li^6$ is $6\cdot01697$ atomic mass units. This atom is supposed to be made from three neutrons, each of mass $1\cdot00893$ and three hydrogen atoms of mass $1\cdot00812$. The difference between the original mass and the sum of the constituent masses is $0\cdot03419$, which is a measure of the energy needed to disintegrate the nucleus in mass units. In unstable nuclei, that is to say, the radio-active families, the sum of the masses of the constituent parts, which are here the radio-active products, is less than the original mass, and the difference appears as energy. Because of the factor c^2 in the formula a very small mass difference produces a very large release of energy, and the recent developments of nuclear weapons have demonstrated this fact violently.

Time-keeping with Constant Acceleration

Returning to the treatment of motion with constant acceleration, we now have an expression for the velocity in terms of the time in motion with constant acceleration g, and this expression is not very different from the Newtonian expression $v = gt$, except for very high velocities. But it does have the advantage from our point of view that it prevents the velocity ever getting as high as that of light, even though the acceleration is constant (*Figure 37*). We now need

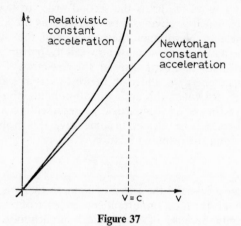

Figure 37

to find an expression for the distance gone in a certain time, and again this is not quite so easy as in the Newtonian case. The easiest thing for our purposes will be to verify a result, which can be found by other means which we need not concern ourselves with. If we consider the expression

$$\left(x + \frac{1}{g}\right)^2 = \frac{1}{g^2} + t^2,$$

where the constant $1/g^2$ has been inserted simply to make x and t vanish together, then we can see, by taking two values of t fairly close together and two values of x similarly, that the difference between this equation with the first value of x, x_1, and the corresponding equation with x_2 written for x will be

$$(x_1 - x_2)\left(x_1 + x_2 + \frac{2}{g}\right) = (t_1 - t_2)(t_1 + t_2).$$

This gives the average speed between the two positions as

$$\frac{x_1 - x_2}{t_1 - t_2} \simeq \frac{t}{x + \dfrac{1}{g}} = \frac{gt}{\sqrt{1 + (gt)^2}},$$

(when t_1 and t_2 are close together) which is exactly the expression for the speed which we have already had in movement with constant acceleration. It follows that the expression which we have given for distance in terms of time is the appropriate one for motion with constant acceleration. A moment's consideration will show that it agrees very closely with the Newtonian one, although this is not obvious on the surface. For if we multiply out the left-hand side we shall derive terms independent of the acceleration and terms divided by the acceleration. Because of the system of units which we are employing, the terms divided by the acceleration are actually very large compared with the ones independent of it, and therefore we can neglect the term x^2 altogether, and we get the usual result in Newtonian Mechanics that the distance gone is $\frac{1}{2}gt^2$.

We can now return to the clock paradox problem and give the promised discussion in terms of accelerated observers. To do this we must set up an arrangement of equivalent observers which are uniformly accelerating relative to each other. The problem here is very much like the problem which we considered when we set up the transformation between two observers in uniform relative motion. Of course, in that case the two observers were both inertial observers, but it is curious that this fact is not used in finding the transformation between them. We *do* use the fact that if one of them is inertial then the other one will be as well, in the form that their velocity of separation is constant, but we do not use the fact that the first one is actually inertial. In the present case, of course, one of the observers can be inertial but the other one will then certainly not be, and in general neither of them will be.

We suppose that one of the observers sends a signal at time t_1 to the other who receives it at time t'_1 and re-transmits it, and it is then received back by the first observer at time t_2. The first observer therefore *assigns* a time of $\frac{1}{2}(t_1 + t_2)$ to the instant of reflection and the distance away of the second observer at that time of $\frac{1}{2}(t_2 - t_1)$. The distance and time of the second observer must be such that he is moving with constant acceleration g and therefore we conclude that

$$x = \frac{1}{g}\sqrt{1 + (gt)^2} - \frac{1}{g},$$

which becomes when we substitute for x and t in terms of the times of transmission and reception of the signal

$$g(t_2 - t_1) + 2 = \sqrt{4 + g^2(t_2 + t_1)^2}.$$

This simplifies to the form $\dfrac{1}{t_1} - \dfrac{1}{t_2} = g$, which tells us the required relation between the times of transmission and reception of the signal. The corresponding relation in the uniform velocity case was $t_2 = k^2 t_1$ where k represented the velocity in some sense. Here it is the reciprocals of the times which give us an equation most easily understood. We now have to put in the condition that the two observers are *equivalent*, and this is the condition which corresponds to that place, in the consideration of uniformly separating observers, where we remarked that the time variable of the second observer for the instant of reflection is kt_1 and then the time of the first observer for the receiving of the signal back again is $k^2 t_1$, so that the relationship between the observers is symmetrical; that is to say, in our present notation, $t_1' = kt_1$ and t_2 is also kt_1', when they are uniformly separating.

Here they are not uniformly separating but $\dfrac{1}{t_1} - \dfrac{1}{t_2}$ is equal to g. This equation is in a form which is exactly suitable to express the symmetry between the observers. We have to express t'_1 as a function of t_1, say

$$t_1' = f(t_1),$$

of such a form that also

$$t_2 = f(t_1'),$$

and yet

$$\frac{1}{t_2} = \frac{1}{t_1} - g.$$

It is obvious that one solution is

$$\frac{1}{t_1'} = \frac{1}{t_1} - \frac{1}{2}g,$$

and this is, in fact, the only one which is continuous.

The first thing that we have now to do is to see how to calculate the corresponding ratio to k where the velocities are now changing. Since $\dfrac{1}{t_1} - \dfrac{1}{t_2} = g$ we have also, a moment later, when t_1 and t_2

are each increased say to $t_1 + h_1$ and $t_2 + h_2$, a similar equation

$$\frac{1}{t_1 + h_1} - \frac{1}{t_2 + h_2} = g,$$

which gives us by comparison the equation

$$\frac{h_1}{t_1(t_1 + h_1)} = \frac{h_2}{t_2(t_2 + h_2)},$$

and therefore the ratio of h_2 to h_1 is roughly $t_2{}^2$ to $t_1{}^2$. This then is the ratio corresponding to k^2 in the previous case, so that the ratio corresponding to k is t_2/t_1. This enables us to write down very easily the quantity $k + \frac{1}{k}$ which would determine the amount that a clock goes slow in the former case when the velocity was constant, and we may compare the actual rate at which the clock goes slow, in this case with this quantity, which will have the value $\frac{t_1}{t_2} + \frac{t_2}{t_1}$. In order to determine the rate at which a clock actually goes slow we have to calculate the time assigned to the event of reflection by the first observer and compare it with the time actually given to this event by the second observer. The time given to the event by the second observer is t_1' and the other time is $\frac{1}{2}(t_1 + t_2)$. By comparing these two we shall be able to find out the rate at which the clock actually goes slow in this case.

Although the motion is not uniform, the quantity k is still a very useful way of carrying out the calculations.

Let t_1, t_2 be times measured by the first observer, t_1' that measured by the second and t the time allotted to the instant of reflection by the first observer. If t_1 increases slightly to $t_1 + h_1$, suppose that all the others change slightly to $t_2 + h_2$, $t_1' + h_1'$ and $t + h$.

Since
$$\frac{1}{t_1} - \frac{1}{t_2} = g,$$

and
$$\frac{1}{t_1 + h_1} - \frac{1}{t_2 + h_2} = g,$$

we have by subtraction, as before,

$$\frac{h_1}{t_1(t_1 + h_1)} = \frac{h_2}{t_2(t_2 + h_2)},$$

so that if h_1, and therefore h_2 is very small, $\dfrac{h_2}{h_1} = \dfrac{t_2{}^2}{t_1{}^2}$ and this is the quantity k^2, so that $t_2 = kt_1$.

4

Now $\qquad$ $t = \tfrac{1}{2}(t_1 + t_2),$

so that $\qquad$ $t + h = \tfrac{1}{2}(t_1 + t_2 + h_1 + h_2),$

and so $\qquad$ $h = \tfrac{1}{2}(h_1 + h_2)$

or $\qquad$ $\dfrac{h}{h_1} = \tfrac{1}{2}(1 + k^2) = k\beta$

where β is the quantity entering in the Lorentz transformations,

$$\beta = \frac{1}{2}\left(k + \frac{1}{k}\right),$$

which measures the rate at which clocks go slow.

On the other hand, in exactly the same way as with h_2/h_1 we can show that

$$h_1'/h_1 = t_1'^2/t_1^2.$$

Now $\qquad$ $\dfrac{1}{t_1} - \dfrac{1}{t_1'} = \dfrac{1}{2}g,$

so that $\quad \dfrac{t_1}{t_1'} = 1 - \dfrac{1}{2}gt_1 = \dfrac{1}{2} + \dfrac{1}{2}(1 - gt_1) = \dfrac{1}{2}\left(1 + \dfrac{1}{k}\right),$

since $\qquad$ $\dfrac{t_1}{t_2} = 1 - gt_1 = \dfrac{1}{k}.$

It follows that

$$\frac{h_1'}{h_1} = \frac{4k^2}{(1 + k)^2},$$

so that

$$\frac{h_1}{h_1'} = \frac{1}{4}\frac{(1 + k)^2}{k}\,\beta = \left[\frac{1}{2}\left(\sqrt{k} + \frac{1}{\sqrt{k}}\right)\right]^2 \beta = \frac{1}{2}\,\beta(\beta + 1),$$

which is always greater than β. This is to say, the rate at which a moving clock goes slow is greater at each instant in the case of uniform acceleration then for the corresponding uniformly moving clock. The difference can be seen in the following table or in the graph (*Figure 38*):

TABLE OF $\beta = \dfrac{1}{\sqrt{1 - v^2}}$ AND $\tfrac{1}{2}\beta(\beta + 1)$

v	β	$\tfrac{1}{2}\beta(\beta + 1)$
$\tfrac{1}{2}$	1·16	1·24
$\tfrac{3}{4}$	1·51	1·90
$\tfrac{7}{8}$	2·07	3·18

There is, then, no doubt that a uniform acceleration (and so presumably any acceleration) will make a difference to the clock paradox argument, contrary to some statements that have been made, but the difference is such as to increase the paradox, not to lessen it.

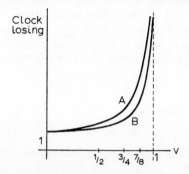

Figure 38 Slowness of clocks plotted against velocity v
A. For motion with constant acceleration.
B. For motion with constant velocity.

Particles of Zero Rest-Mass

Let us return to the question of the variation of mass with velocity. The rest-mass of a particle moving with given energy E is $m_0 = CE$ where $C = \frac{1}{\beta} = \sqrt{1 - v^2}$. If we consider particles with faster and faster velocities (although, of course, with $|v| \leq 1$) they will (if they have the given energy) have smaller and smaller rest-masses. It is possible to imagine a particle in relativity with zero rest-mass (and its velocity must then be that of light). Such a particle then has a momentum $p = E$ (since $E^2 - p^2 = m_0^2$).

In Newtonian mechanics it was impossible even to imagine a particle with zero mass and finite energy and momentum, for there $E = \frac{1}{2}mv^2$, $p = mv$, so that if $m \to 0$, $v \to \infty$ then $E/p = \frac{1}{2}v$, so that not both E and p can be finite, non-zero. One of the successes of relativity is that two such zero-mass particles are observed—one of them being the particle-form of light, the photon. The other, the neutrino, is a little more recondite, and we will consider it later. In its wave-form, light is thought of as having a definite frequency; the connexion between the two descriptions was discovered by Planck in 1899—a stream of light of fixed frequency v is to be described as a stream of photons of energy (and therefore momentum) $E = hv$. When light is scattered by materials of low atomic weight, it is changed in frequency (a fact noticed first by Compton in 1923 and called the Compton effect). The essential effect is a collision between a photon and a *free* electron, but in materials of low atomic weight the electrons are only lightly bound, and may be treated as free. The actual frequency change depends on the angle at which the photon is scattered, but we shall confine our attention to two special cases, in both of which the whole motion is in a straight line. If the photon is incident with energy, and momentum, hv, and continues on its way (after pushing the electron on with energy and momentum m, mu) with energy hv, then from the constancy of the energy

$$m_0 + hv_0 = m + hv,$$

and from the momentum

$$hv_0 = mu + hv,$$

where $m^2(1 - u^2) = m_0^2$, if m_0 is the rest-mass of the electron. Thus

$$[m_0 + h(v_0 - v)]^2 - [h(v_0 - v)]^2 = m_0^2,$$

which gives $v_0 = v$, so there is no change of frequency. If, however, the photon bounces back with momentum hv backwards, the second equation becomes

$$hv_0 = mu - hv,$$

so that

$$[m_0 + h(v_0 - v)]^2 - [h(v_0 + v)]^2 = m_0^2,$$

which gives, easily,

$$\frac{1}{v} - \frac{1}{v_0} = \frac{2h}{m_0}$$

Between these two extremes there is a frequency change between zero and $2h/m_0$.

Important as the Compton effect is, as an application of relativity, it does not provide such a critical test of the theory, because it is possible to provide approximate accounts of it by Newtonian mechanics. Such accounts cannot, of course, introduce zero mass photons, but, although implausible, they are possible, and to this extent the Compton effect is not an accurate test of the theory.

A much more striking instance of the zero mass property came in 1956 when Lee and Yang suggested the now famous experiments on the "non-conservation of parity". There are more experimental details of these in the next chapter; here we simply wish to point out the essential feature. Many of the particles considered in quantum theory possess *spin*. For the present purposes it will not be too inaccurate to think of them as tiny spinning spheres. If such a particle is moving in a certain direction, with its spin in the same direction, like a small spinning corkscrew (with a right-handed screw) according to one observer, we can find another observer for whom it is a similar left-handed corkscrew. We have only to reverse the velocity of the particle; if originally it is moving with speed v and the new observer is moving with speed V relative to the first, the Einstein velocity formula

$$\frac{v + V}{1 + vV}$$

gives $-v$ if

$$v + V + v(1 + vV) = 0,$$

which is equivalent to

$$V = -\frac{2v}{1 + v^2}.$$

Now if the neutrino (which has spin) is observed by one observer to be right-handed, this reversal is impossible for it. For since its rest-mass is zero, $v = 1$, so that V would also be the speed of light, and the transformation is impossible. Similarly a left-handed neutrino could never become right-handed. It is therefore perfectly possible for only one of these kinds of neutrino to exist without conflicting with our ideas of the background. This was the state of affairs found by the experiments suggested by Lee and Yang.

Decay of Elementary Particles

As we shall see in the next chapter, one of the most surprising discoveries of the last 30 years in physics is that of the existence of numerous "elementary particles" which decay after a short life into other such particles. It will be instructive to work out the decay of such a particle here, especially as we need the results in the last chapter.

We can look at the decay from the point of view of an observer with respect to whom the particle is at rest, so that its initial energy and momentum are $(E, 0)$. If it decays into two particles (a common case, and one of most interest to us, as well as being typical) we can suppose their masses to be m_1, m_2, with energies E_1, E_2. Since the total momentum is conserved, the two particles must have momenta p, $-p$. Then

$$E = E_1 + E_2,$$
$$E_1^2 - p^2 = m_1^2, \qquad E_2^2 - p^2 = m_2^2,$$

and the second pair of equations give

$$m_1^2 - m_2^2 = E_1^2 - E_2^2.$$

Dividing by the first equation,

$$\frac{m_1{}^2 - m_2{}^2}{E} = E_1 - E_2,$$

so that, adding and subtracting,

$$E_1 = \frac{1}{2}\left[E + \frac{m_1{}^2 - m_2{}^2}{E}\right],$$

$$E_2 = \frac{1}{2}\left[E - \frac{m_1{}^2 - m_2{}^2}{E}\right].$$

The momentum transferred is then given by

$$p^2 = E_1{}^2 - m_1{}^2$$

$$= \frac{1}{4}\left[E^2 + \frac{(m_1{}^2 - m_2{}^2)^2}{E^2} - 2(m_1{}^2 + m_2{}^2)\right]$$

$$= \frac{1}{4E^2}[E^2 - (m_1 + m_2)^2]\,[E^2 - (m_1 - m_2)^2].$$

Since this must be positive, or at worst zero, we see that $m_1 + m_2$ cannot exceed E, but it can be less than E, the corresponding energy then being in the form of kinetic energy, the momentum being correspondingly more.

The new environment, then, which our discussions have elaborated leads to particles of zero rest-mass, a change in our ideas of symmetry between left and right, as well as a description of mass as energy, part of which can be released and turned to practical use. It will be abundantly clear to the reader that our search for the environment is leading us more and more to the realm of the very small. So far we have said little about quantum theory, but now we have to take up this other side of the story. In the next chapter we shall consider the experimental facts which are most important for our purposes and then draw conclusions from them in the last chapter.

CHAPTER 6

ELEMENTARY PARTICLES

General Relativity

In the previous chapters we have traced the development of the idea of the environment and the system reacting with it to more and more refined applications of this conception. We began with the idea of absolute space and we saw how Newtonian Mechanics was forced into the position of rejecting absolute space and accepting instead as its background the collection of all inertial observers, all those observers being in uniform motion relative to each other. But it was able, because it did not carry out a full analysis of how we assign times to distant events, to retain an absolute time. When we carry out this analysis of the assigning of times to distant events we have to adopt the set of inertial observers as described by Einstein in Special Relativity, and so we have a further refinement of the background, in which not only are the observers moving relative to each other, but their time reckonings for distant events are slightly different. This more refined background only differs from the Newtonian background for very high velocities and so the most interesting application of it will naturally be to particles which can move very quickly.

It may happen that the situations which arise in astronomy can lead to circumstances in which relativity theory is of importance. But those circumstances are associated not so much with very high velocities as with very strong gravitational fields. Now we have said very little so far about gravitation except in Newtonian theory. There is a fairly obvious extension of the theory of relativity which we have been discussing so far to include gravitation, and so we can construct a complete relativistic theory of gravitation. This is the general theory of relativity which was put forward by Einstein in 1915, ten years after his construction of the special theory. Whereas in the case of the special theory it is possible to argue that the ideas were current at the time and had in fact been formulated by various people before Einstein, in the case of the general theory there is no doubt that the credit is his alone.

The general theory is an extremely technical mathematical device for writing the equations of gravitation in a way which does not depend upon the observers, and we shall not be concerned with it at all in this book, for it does not lend itself to the kind of treatment which we wish to give here. Moreover, it does not illuminate any further the idea of the interaction of a system with its environment; the only difference is that the description of the environment assumed in special relativity is, in the general theory, only supposed to apply locally, (as was explained at the end of chapter 2). Another observer would construct his environment in a way somewhat different from ours, the most obvious analogy being that of a number of two-dimensional people living on the surface of a sphere, say on the surface of the earth. At any point on the surface of the earth the local lines of latitude and longitude form a convenient rectangular coordinate system. But suppose that we continue those lines to a nearby point, treating them as "straight lines", that is to say, as great circles on the surface of a sphere, (the intersection of a plane through the centre of the earth with the sphere). We shall find that, although the parallels of longitude at a nearby point are again the coordinate lines running north and south, the parallels of latitude are not. This is because the lines of latitude, except for the equator, are not great circles but so-called small circles, that is, they are plane sections of the earth by planes which do not pass through the centre. If we try to set up a rectangular coordinate system at all points on the sphere, we are bound to fail. We may be able to extend it over a certain region but we shall always run up against a point which we have been to before, and at which the rectangular coordinates which we set up do not agree with the ones which we set up when we were last at that point. This kind of failure to mesh of nearby coordinate systems is the characteristic feature of the general theory, and it will be clear that it needs quite a complicated mathematical treatment to deal with it adequately.

We shall therefore instead confine our attention to a field in which the high velocities involved make the application of special relativity of particular importance, and in this field it will turn out that the idea of the environment, and the interaction with the environment has been carried a step further in a way which is not always fully realised in books on the subject. This is the field of elementary particles.

Non-relativistic Quantum Mechanics

It will be as well to approach this field historically, for if we try to survey it in any other way we are likely to be overwhelmed by the immense amount of experimental material which has to be digested.

Quantum mechanics arose at the turn of the century originally in the question of the equilibrium between radiation and matter at a certain temperature which was explained in chapter 1. But the hypothesis which Planck made in order to explain this equilibrium soon turned out to be one with very many other applications. These applications had not been dreamt of before, because they only occurred in rather subtle and accurate experiments. By one of those curious chances, which is not at all uncommon in the history of science, just when this hypothesis had been made by Planck, such experiments, for quite other reasons, had begun to be performed. In the years from 1900 to 1925 such experiments were more and more elaborated, and many of them were satisfactorily explained by quantum mechanics. It is true that quantum mechanics at that time could not be called a scientific theory in the sense in which we usually use the term; rather it was a scientific art, the practitioners of which required an apprenticeship in order for them to be able to see how to use the tools at their disposal, almost like a mediaeval craftsman learning silversmithing. That is to say, it was not possible initially to make a clear statement of what the assumptions of the theory were and then to work their consequences out in the way in which it has proved possible to do with special relativity.

The theory changed very much in 1926, and in fact it is really more appropriate to speak of the quantum theory after 1926 as being a completely different theory which explained much the same facts as before 1926. In 1926 Heisenberg and Schrödinger both put forward explanations of quantum phenomena which were apparently quite different but in fact turned out to be mathematically equivalent. We shall not need to consider these explanations in detail but it is worth mentioning them here so as to get an idea of the time scale in the various discoveries. The essential feature of both Heisenberg and Schrödinger's methods of explaining quantum phenomena was that they were only consistent with Newtonian relativity; that is to say, they assumed an absolute time if one changed to another inertial observer. The equations would be unchanged so long as the time was unchanged, but if the time were changed, according to the Lorentz transformation, then something quite different resulted from the original equations. Accordingly, one could definitely say that quantum mechanics as formulated by Schrödinger and Heisenberg in 1926 was at variance with special relativity and as such must be considered an unsatisfactory theory.

Dirac's Equation

This situation was put right in 1928 by Dirac. He showed how to re-formulate the equations of Schrödinger in particular, (although he also explained how Heisenberg's formulation would need to be altered) in such a way that the new equation was equivalent to Schrödinger's under the circumstances in which it had been tested. But the new equation was of such a kind that two inertial observers, between whom the transformation was a special relativistic one, would find the same results for every experiment. We do not wish to enter into the details of Dirac's formulation, but there is one particular feature of it which we have to look at rather more carefully. We can see this feature equally well, not by constructing the whole theory, but simply by thinking of the relativistic description of a particle. We have already explained that the mass of a particle will not be constant in special relativity and we have derived the formula

$$m = \frac{m_0}{\sqrt{1 - v^2}}.$$

We also explained how Einstein interpreted the mass as giving the energy, the mass when the velocity is zero being the rest energy of the particle, and this way of looking at things has been completely vindicated by the physicists who have managed to extract some of the rest energy in the case of unstable nuclei. If E is the energy of the particle, which is actually the same as its mass, and if p is its momentum, we have then that $p = mv$ and $m^2 - m^2v^2 = m_0^2$, and therefore we can at once see that $E^2 = m^2 = m_0^2 + p^2$. The importance of this equation is that it shows that although both E and p change when we go from one inertial observer to another, $E^2 - p^2$ does not change. It is in fact an invariant quantity, because it is the square of the mass of the particle measured by an inertial observer with respect to whom the particle is at rest, and there is only one such inertial observer.

Now, from the point of view of understanding the difficulties which Dirac's equation led to, we should write this in another form, as $E = (m_0^2 + p^2)^{\frac{1}{2}}$, which tells us the energy which a particle must have when it is moving with a momentum p. This equation contains a square root. At first one might think that there was no great difficulty over this; it is true, of course, that every number has two square roots of opposite signs, but the natural reaction would be to make some proviso that the positive sign of square root should be chosen. This was no doubt originally the idea of Dirac, because in the equation which he formulated there is, in effect, a square root of exactly this kind corresponding to two signs of the energy. The equation that Dirac formulated was intended to describe the electron, that is to say, one of those particles which were known, from early in the century, to form part of the atoms of every element. The atom consisted of a central nucleus, which is positively charged and a number of electrons going round it, as it was thought at that time, in orbits very much like the planets going round the sun. This rather simple picture was regarded as hardly tenable after 1926 when the quantum theory was re-formulated, but it is still a useful one to think of. However we think of these electrons, they were there as part of the atoms, and in the description of the electron formulated by Dirac there is a quantity, the energy which arises by a square root of exactly this kind.

Klein's Paradox

We always think of the energy of a particle as positive, but in 1929, that is, in the year following Dirac's discovery of his equation, Klein was able to show that this interpretation, in which the energy is restricted to positive values, led to considerable difficulties. The particle must be thought of as having energy states, and the two states of energy corresponding to the positive and negative values of the square root would be two energy states. The commonsense point of view would be to say that a particle could only be in positive energy states. What Klein showed was that one could certainly imagine, and indeed perhaps construct in practice, experiments which would cause a particle which was in a negative energy state to jump into a positive energy state. This meant that the negative energy states could no longer be neglected; it was impossible to separate out the negative from the positive energy states for good. If one did carry out this separation at one time, particles which were on one side of the fence would later come back on to the other side of the fence, and would have to be taken into consideration.

The way in which Dirac got out of this difficulty was by an ingenious trick known as the Hole theory, which he formulated in 1931. Here he freely admitted the existence of the negative energy states, but he defined the vacuum as a situation where, while of course all the positive energy states were empty, as one would expect, all the negative energy states were fully occupied. Now, in such a situation, if one supplies enough energy from outside, say by means of an electromagnetic field, it is possible that an electron could jump from a negative energy state to a positive energy state, and become observable as an electron. Such a jump is indeed the sort of thing imagined by Klein. When this happens a hole is left behind, and since this hole was formerly filled with a negative charge and was then regarded as part of the vacuum, the *hole* will manifest itself in observation as a positive charge. Thus the Hole theory as formulated in 1931 required the existence of another particle with the same mass as the electron but of opposite charge. This was the positron. This particle has since been observed. In the same way, since Dirac's equation also described the proton, it predicted a particle of the same mass as the proton with negative charge.

As a matter of fact the Hole theory was later discarded in favour of another theory which was thought at the time to be mathematically preferable, that is to say quantum field theory, but it was not superseded until it had done its work. Not only had it predicted the existence of at least two new particles, and more than this could hardly be expected from any theory, but it had also predicted the phenomenon of *pair creation*; that is to say, if energy is supplied so that the electron jumps from a negative to a positive state and appears as an electron, there also appears a positron. From the point of view of electro-magnetic theory the positron was a necessity, because charge had to be conserved no matter what happened. If a negative charge is produced, then a positive charge must be produced with it, but the number of particles no longer had to be conserved; there would now be two particles where there were previously none. Any later theory was bound to include pair creation and annihilation. Quantum field theory was put forward in 1929 and is a mathematical theory of immense complexity. We shall be no more concerned with this here than we shall be concerned with the general theory of relativity, but it is probably not too misleading to think of quantum field theory as a rather high-powered version of the Hole theory, which has managed by mathematical devices to get rid of the *ad hoc* idea of the hole altogether. Although the quantum field theory appeared at the time to be more successful and mathematically preferable to the Hole theory, the present situation is that it has been a rather miserable failure in nearly all its applications.

Pair Creation

It would be a good idea here to use the ideas which we have found already to find out just how much energy has to be supplied in pair creation. Before we can do this we must work out a little more about mechanics than we have worked out before. The momentum which we found earlier, which was *mv* where *m* is the mass, duly increased by the velocity, is something which would be conserved in a collision process; that is to say that the total momentum of the ingoing particles is equal to the total momentum of the outgoing particles. It is true that we found this momentum in terms of the acceleration by noting that the acceleration was the rate of change of momentum, and this was because we originally formed these mechanical ideas on the basis of particles acted on by forces. Now it is a striking fact, and one which is not merely accidental, but of considerable importance in the theory, that almost all that we know about elementary particles is about collision processes. The number of experiments in which one sees elementary particles acted on by forces in any conventional sense is very much smaller than those in which one sees them hitting each other and changing into other particles. And if we set on one side that particular instance in which we see a particle moving in a crossed electric and magnetic field, and so moving in a curved path because of its charge (an experiment which does nothing but determine the charge on the particle) then we can say that, apart from that special case, all the evidence which we have about elementary particles is from collision processes. It is natural then that we should be much more concerned with the mechanics of collision processes than with the sort of mechanics where a particle accelerates under the influence of a force.

Let us then investigate a particular mechanical problem, and while we are investigating it we shall be able to derive the sort of mechanics which will be appropriate for other problems on the way. Our problem is how much energy to supply to a beam of, say, protons, which is incident on a proton at rest in the laboratory, in order to produce pair creation. In other words, after the collision, as well as having the two protons which were there to start with, a proton and anti-proton pair also are to be found. Beforehand the situation is that the energy and momentum of the incident particle is, say, E and p and the energy of the proton at rest is, say m_0 and its momentum 0 according to an observer at rest in the laboratory. It would be more convenient after the collision to look at things from the point of view of an observer with respect to whom all the particles had no resultant momentum. This is the so-called centre-of-mass observer. There will then be a total energy afterwards corresponding to the four masses and a total momentum of zero. We always treat these collision processes in a way which would be described in classical mechanics as elastic collisions; that is to say, we assume not only that the total momentum before and after is the same but also that the total energy is the same. The total energy beforehand is $E + m_0$ and the total momentum is p, so that $(E + m_0)^2 - p^2$ is a quantity which is the same whichever observer we consider. It follows that $(E + m_0)^2 - p^2$ is equal to the corresponding quantity after impact, which is $(4m_0)^2$, if we suppose that we are seeking the *least* energy needed for the process, which produces the 4 particles at rest, and of course $E^2 - p^2$ we know to be m_0^2 in any case. From these equations it follows at once by subtraction that E has to be $7m_0$ and therefore that the actual kinetic energy supplied to the particle has to be $6m_0$, the rest of the energy simply being the rest energy. This is the sort of calculation which can be very quickly carried out provided we use the fact that $E^2 - p^2$ is a quantity which is the same for all observers.

It is as well here to take up a point which will be useful later. We have largely confined ourselves in our treatment of relativity to one-dimensional problems—particles moving along a straight line.

Naturally the theory has to be extended beyond this, and it is quite possible to do so, but it would lead us astray to do so here. There is, however, one result for general motion which we shall need; the expression $E^2 - p^2$ is also the rest-mass (and therefore invariant) even when p represents the magnitude of the momentum in a motion which is not along a straight line. This is because, at any instant, the momentum is in *some* direction and we could imagine an observer who takes this direction as the one in which he draws the line along which he measures distance. In changing from the measurements of one observer to those of another at rest relative to the first, who has drawn his axes in different directions, the magnitude p is unchanged, and so in the general case $E^2 - p^2$ is unchanged.

The Feynman Picture of Pair Creation

If we use again the conservation of energy in this way, we can see how pair creation could perhaps have been foreseen even without the full analysis that is provided by Dirac's equation and Klein's paradox, if we look a little more closely at some of the problems considered in ordinary Newtonian mechanics. Let us consider the problem in which particles are shot from a point A to a point B, there being, in between these two points, a field of force which tries to slow the particles down. It will be as well to idealise this situation a little so that the calculations are more straightforward, although the ideal situation which we are describing is not the only one which shows the effect; the effect will be shown for all fields which are sufficiently strong. The idealised situation is that in which the particle moving from one point to another meets a barrier which reduces its speed as it moves from v to u, the decrease for different velocities v being defined by postulating a constant difference of kinetic energy. This barrier is a certain thickness, and at the other end of the barrier its speed is again increased to the value which it had formerly. When we draw this situation in a space-time diagram of the sort to which we have been accustomed, we see the path of the particle before the barrier as a straight line, and after the barrier as a parallel straight line, and then the path through the barrier, since it has a smaller velocity, will be a straight line which is at a smaller angle to the upward axis than the other lines. The problem of sending the particle from one point to another is equivalent to the problem of drawing two parallel straight lines through the two points in such a way that their ends at the barriers can be joined by another straight line whose angle is determined by the amount that the velocity has changed. The solution $APQB$ which is shown in *Figure 39* is the one which immediately occurs to us but as far as the equations are concerned there is another solution, $ARSB$, which is also shown in *Figure 39.* At first sight this second solution seems to be nonsense, for in it one of the paths, that is the path of the particle through the barrier, corresponds to the particle going backwards in time. Now we could interpret a solution like this in

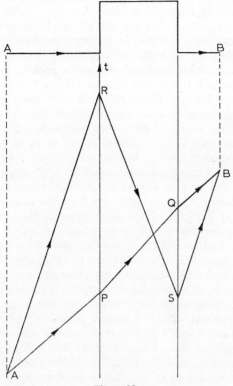

Figure 39

terms of pair creation in the following way. We could say that at a certain time a particle left *A.* A certain time later there was pair creation at *S* of a particle which proceeds to *B* and an anti-particle proceeding to *R.* At *R* the anti-particle meets with the particle which was emitted at *A* and the two annihilate each other; thus the particle which was, in the previous description, an ordinary particle going backwards in time is now described as an anti-particle going forwards in time; that is to say, the negative energy solutions are also describable as particles of positive energy going backwards in time. This second solution sounds rather fanciful when we first describe it, and I think would not be taken seriously if it were not for the fact that it has turned out to be equally important. In fact pair creation makes the two solutions exactly of equivalent value.

Discovery of more Elementary Particles

Let us now turn to the other prediction of the Hole theory which we mentioned, the existence of other elementary particles, and consider the developments that this has led to. Until 1931 there were only two elementary particles in quantum mechanics, the electron and the proton. In the hydrogen atom an electron went round the central nucleus which consisted of a single proton. In the case of more complicated atoms, say that of helium, we already have a slight problem because although the helium atom has only two orbiting electrons so that the central nucleus has to have a charge of two units, the weight of the central nucleus appears to be that of four protons; that is to say, there is not so much charge in the nucleus as expected, and at first people thought that perhaps this was due to there being electrons sealed up in the nucleus. But this explanation had to give way to an alternative one in 1932, when Chadwick showed that one could get from the nucleus of suitable atoms neutral particles of the same mass as the proton. These so-called neutrons had actually been thought of as early as 1920, but because they had no charge, it was very difficult to observe them. In the same year, 1932, the prediction of Dirac about the positron was also verified and positrons were observed in a Wilson cloud-chamber (that is, in an evacuated chamber containing water vapour in unstable conditions, so that a slight disturbance causes it to condense into droplets). Where a particle passes through the chamber, a string of water droplets is produced, and the corresponding track on a photographic plate is used to determine various properties of the particle. Anderson, in 1932, found the track which corresponded to the creation of an electron-positron pair; it should be mentioned here that, contrary to the implied suggestion in many accounts, Anderson had no intention of seeking the Dirac positron. He seems to have been unaware of Dirac's prediction; he was carrying out a detailed investigation into cosmic-ray phenomena, and at first interpreted the positively-charged tracks as protons, but was forced to another hypothesis later by difficulties in making mass-values consistent. The positron in Anderson's picture was annihilated almost at once by combination with another electron. Thus the position was in 1932 that four particles had been found.

The next contribution, in 1934, was the definite establishment of a fifth particle with the curious property that its rest mass was zero. This was the neutrino, which had originally been introduced in order to make it possible for energy and momentum to be conserved

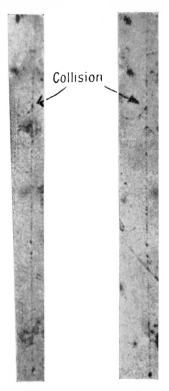

Figure 40 (*a*)   The earliest mass-measurement of a heavier (*K*) meson. (By permission of the Institute of Physics and the Physical Society, and L. Leprince-Ringuet.)

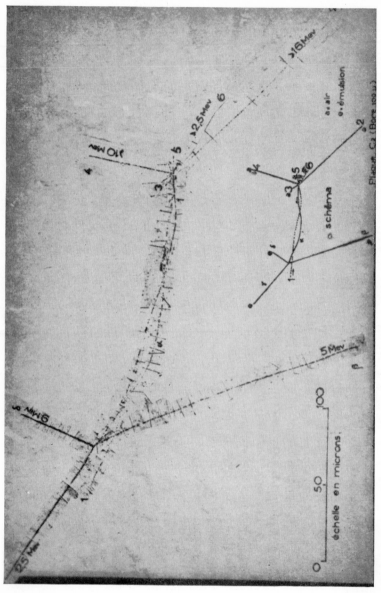

Figure 40 (*b*) Reconstruction of a collision establishing the definite existence of a *K*-meson. (By permission of the American Institute of Physics and L. Leprince-Ringuet.)

in a particular kind of nuclear disintegration. The full theory of this disintegration was worked out by Fermi in 1934 and although it was very difficult to observe a neutrino, its existence was taken by then to fairly well established. Neither the neutrino nor the anti-proton, which was also predicted by Dirac, were observed directly until comparatively recently. When so many particles have arisen the idea of them being elementary is slightly less clear than it was; it is more a question of what properties should constitute an elementary particle, than of deciding which ones are elementary. Now an elementary particle is, in the first place, something which cannot be analysed into other elementary particles, and, secondly, and this is really the important characteristic, something which has an exhaustible set of attributes. If we try to think how such a particle differs from, for instance, a cricket ball, we can say that a cricket ball can never be described completely; we can talk about its hardness, what shade of red it is, its size and weight and shape and so on, and yet when we have stated all those properties, if we take two cricket balls which have all these properties in common, we can still imagine sufficiently careful experiments which will detect a difference between them. But the elementary particles are specified completely by giving their charge and mass and speed and some other properties like that. Some of these other properties are not very easy to describe in everyday terms, but they are properties which are fully described by giving values to a number which can only have one of two or three values.

Nuclear Forces

This question of how many elementary particles there are became very much more serious from 1935 onwards. The question which gave rise to modern developments was how it was that the nucleus held together. It was known that the nucleus consisted of protons and neutrons. There were as many protons as there were positive charges in the nucleus, and since, in electro-statics, similar charges repel each other, one would have expected that all the protons in the nucleus would have repelled each other very strongly and the nucleus would have been shattered. But in fact the nucleus is an astonishingly stable system, so that, it was argued, there must be some new field of force which is holding the particle together in the nucleus. Gravitational forces were much too weak, and so this new field, since it could be neither gravitational nor electro-magnetic, had to be some new kind of field. But this new kind of field was never observed outside the nucleus, so it followed that the field must have a very short range, and fall off very rapidly outside the nuclear region. In fact, it was found to have a range of about

10^{-13} cm. A field, in quantum mechanics, can also be described in a particle form, and so the field in this case would correspond to a certain particle. By determining experimentally the range that the nuclear field had to have, one could determine the corresponding mass of the particle. The mass turned out to be about two hundred times the electron mass, and the elaboration of the hypothesis, that such a short-lived particle should exist, was the meson theory of Yukawa. Yukawa also took advantage of the possibility that the new particles could be short-lived to explain more of the available experimental information. It is possible to produce the nuclear forces by short-lived unstable particles because the way in which a quantum field is described by particles is by *exchange*. A *force* between particles is a way of stating that the motion of one particle is influenced by the other; in the case of an exchange force one particle emits a meson, so that its momentum is changed accordingly and the meson is absorbed by the other particle and so changes *its* momentum. Since the particles are packed so closely together in the nucleus (an average distance apart being $r = 10^{-13}$ cm) the exchange *could* be carried out by very light particles travelling with the velocity of light and existing for only $\dfrac{r}{c} = 10^{-23}$ sec. However, because of the range of the forces we need heavier particles and so a somewhat longer life-time. By considering all the evidence it was possible for Yukawa to estimate the meson life-time as 10^{-8} sec. When, in the following year, the cloud-chamber photographs showed the existence of a particle of mass about two hundred electron masses, it was at once thought that the Yukawa meson had actually been observed. A great deal of work then went into the observation of elementary particles, and by 1942 difficulties had arisen. The numerical values which people had been able to attach to the meson observations just could not be made to tie up any more, (for instance, the life-time was wrong by a factor of 100) and so a two-meson theory was formulated. This was experimentally confirmed by the group of physicists, (one can no longer talk of individual discoverers) who were working at Bristol in 1947, with photographs of cosmic ray showers.

It is interesting to consider how this two-meson theory came to be discovered. By 1947 it was already becoming obvious that further research on these particles necessitated the building of very large machines in order to produce particles by such processes as pair creation. The amount of energy for these processes was very large, and so the machines were extremely expensive. In England immediately after the war there was no money available to build big machines, and so Powell in Bristol had to work out a different method of carrying on what interested him, and he found a beautiful method of studying cosmic rays.

He analysed the minute lines which appear on photographic plates which are left unexposed in places fairly high up, either on mountain tops or in balloons, for some weeks. These minute lines are in fact particle tracks of very much the same kind as one finds in the cloud-chamber, only in this case the tracks are produced in the photographic emulsion. From these tracks Powell was able to get amazingly detailed information. The two mesons were given names after the Greek letters π and μ and the π-meson, which is the one in the nucleus, (that is to say, the one which may correspond to the one put forward by Yukawa) interacts strongly with the protons in the nucleus. The mesons in the cosmic rays which were now called the μ-mesons, interacted only very weakly with protons, which accounted for the difficulty in making these into the Yukawa mesons. The connection between the two is as follows. The μ-mesons decay after a millionth of a second into electrons. The π-mesons decay in about one hundredth of the lifetime of the μ-mesons into μ-mesons and these mesons then decay as before. A year later π-mesons were produced artificially and since then a great deal of progress has been made in meson physics by means of artificially produced mesons.

Heavier Mesons

A year before this Leprince-Ringuet had observed an event in a cloud-chamber, and he was able, by fairly complicated argument, to show that it was a meson, whose mass was nearly a thousand electron masses (*Figure 40*). Since the π and μ-mesons were very much lighter, this was clearly neither of those, and so a third meson of considerably greater mass had been observed. In the years following various new particles were found, some of them of the same mass as Leprince-Ringuet's, which are now called K-mesons, and some of them of about double that mass and even heavier.

Most recently the experimental evidence has taken a new turn so that the very idea of a particle has been considerably extended, and with this new idea of a particle, which does not really concern us for the present argument, very many new particles have been observed. Depending on how one determines which ones are different versions of the same particle, or essentially different particles, one gets various total numbers of particles, all the systems of classification give a figure somewhere in the region of one hundred. Of course, this is a very serious situation from the point of view of the analysis of matter into elementary particles, for an essential feature of the idea of an elementary particle is that there are not many of these fundamental things. When one has about a hundred it is clear that somehow a new theory will have to arise, which will explain these as variants of a smaller number, but at present we have no such theory. It is as well now to leave the historical development and try to survey the evidence which we have about elementary particles in a more systematic manner, so that we can then come to the point which really interests us, which is the nature of the environment postulated in elementary particle physics.

The Uncertainty Principle

We want, then, to try to explain what the position is in a problem which people have been considering ever since the time of the Greeks, that is to explain all the physical world in terms of the workings of just a few elements, which can occur in a variety of different combinations. The first problem, of course, is to determine what the elements are.

Our knowledge here is extremely limited, and the experiments make it seem more limited each day. Because of this extremely limited understanding of the elements, we are particularly concerned with ideas of the sort which we are going to describe later, about the environment. It seems that one can make a beginning in describing the behaviour of matter in general in terms of a number of elementary particles. About these elementary particles we know very little for certain, because most of the information which we are given about them is interpreted in terms of an extremely complex theory, and the question of whether this theory is indeed correct is already pre-judged if we suppose that the information is interpreted in terms of the theory. There is, it is true, a great deal of experimental information, but the difficulty is to know exactly what it all means.

Many workers in the field believe, however, that the elementary particles satisfy general principles of two kinds. Firstly, the principles of quantum mechanics: for our purposes the essential feature of quantum mechanics is that it involves an uncertainty in measurement. This uncertainty is of an extremely precise kind. It is not just an uncertainty in any measurements, but in particular measurements which are related in a certain way, and the uncertainty is then specified by the Heisenberg uncertainty principle. As an example, if we measure the position of a particle with a certain accuracy, then the accuracy with which can determine its momentum is limited by the condition that the product of the errors in the two cases, where the errors are assessed in some conventional way, should be of the order of a certain number. This number will have the dimensions of distance-times-momentum (naturally), and is about 6.55×10^{-27} c.g.s. units. It is called Planck's constant, because it was introduced by Planck in quite a different way at the very beginning of quantum theory, but the uncertainty principle was not formulated until twenty-five years later.

Elementary particles also obey the requirements of special relativity in the sense that if one changes from one observer to another, and each measures properties of the particles, the transformations have to be made by the Lorentz transformations which we have discussed in earlier chapters. This may at first seem to be a self-evident requirement from our previous analysis. This is not so, for the elementary particles are nothing like the ordinary macroscopic particles, which we were dealing with when we performed our analysis of observations in the earlier chapters. It would be quite conceivable that the correct transformation between inertial observers measuring elementary particles might be quite different and more complicated than the one when they were measuring only billiard balls and such like things. However, it turns out that the situation is not as complicated as it might be, for, as far as we can tell, Lorentz invariance is exactly correct for the description of elementary particles.

Quantum Field Theory

Now we have to find some mathematical theory which will enable us to describe the particles. Until recent years there has been an extremely complicated theory—quantum field theory—which tried to carry out this description. This theory has not had much success, and will probably be superseded soon. Accordingly we shall not describe it at length in this book, but we shall try to give the reader some impression of the theory that is to come, rather than the one that is going. Before doing so, however, it is appropriate to say a few words about the nature of quantum field theory. The easiest way of getting a brief idea of the theory is to say that it is a way of taking an ordinary field theory, for instance the theory of the gravitational field, which we have considered in earlier chapters, and "quantising" this theory. This is the name given to the process of generalising it and altering the way in which it is written so that it conforms to the two general principles which we have been discussing, those of quantum mechanics and of relativity. Then the quantities entering into the field equations, instead of being ordinary forces, as in the case of the gravitational field, are quantities which have a degree of uncertainty in their measurement, and the measures of which by different inertial observers are related by the Lorentz transformation.

Although quantum field theory seems to be on the way out, it has given us a number of exceedingly valuable ideas, and indeed it is really impossible to discuss the theoretical problem except in terms

of the ideas of field theory. According to field theory particles are
entities which have a certain fixed set of attributes. The charge is
one such attribute, and the mass is another, and there are several
other numbers associated with the particle in the same way as the
charge and the mass; but particles also have a relation between
themselves so that two particles are related by something called the
coupling between them. There is more than one kind of coupling,
and some pairs of particles are related by one kind of coupling and
some by another. From the point of view of field theory the purpose
of experiment is to determine the kind of coupling between particles.
According to field theory there is nothing else except particles.
Where one thinks of a field in the ordinary sense, as in the case of an

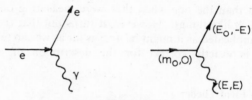

Figure 41

electro-magnetic field, there is also a particle description of the
phenomenon and from the point of view of quantum field theory
this particle description has in many cases certain advantages which
the ordinary field description does not have. As an example, when
one has light, which is of course a form of electro-magnetic radiation,
the particle form is the photon, which is one of those particles with
a zero rest mass. Of course, as we saw before, in special relativity
there is no particular difficulty in the particle having a zero rest mass
so long as its velocity is that of light, for then it is perfectly possible
to arrange for the rest mass to become zero and the velocity to
become that of light in such a way that the mass $\dfrac{m_0}{\sqrt{1-v^2}}$ has any
value one wishes. It is known that excited atoms emit light, and
this was one of the ways in which the fundamental principles of
quantum mechanics was discovered by spectroscopic evidence. The
emission of light by an atom will be represented by a certain coupling.
The atom is, as we know, a central nucleus, with electrons round it,
and the coupling is one in which an electron may be changed into a
combination of an electron and a photon. The photon is then
emitted as light. We can have either an expression,

$$e \leftrightarrow e, \gamma,$$

like an equation or we can have a diagram as shown *Figure 41.* As a matter of fact a single electron cannot emit a photon, as we can see in the following way. Let us analyse the problem according to an observer with respect to whom the electron is originally at rest, so that its energy is its rest mass, m_0, and its momentum is 0. The photon which we wish to emit will have an energy E and so will also have a momentum E since $E^2 - p^2$ is the rest mass, which in this case is zero. In order that momentum may be conserved it follows that the electron which is emitted afterwards must have a momentum $-E$ and an energy say E_0. From conservation of energy and momentum we shall have that $E + E_0 = m_0$ and from the fact that the second electron must have the correct rest mass we have that $E_0{}^2 - E^2 = m^2$. Dividing these two equations gives $E_0 - E = m_0$, so that E is in fact zero, and the photon cannot after all be emitted.

Virtual Processes

There is an interesting way of getting round this difficulty, which is permitted by quantum mechanics. In quantum mechanics it is possible to have a situation, which, if it lasted long enough, would conflict with the conservation of energy. The time for which such a situation is allowed to last in quantum mechanics is determined by the same uncertainty principle which we were speaking of just now. If the amount of energy by which the conservation of energy is broken is E then the process must not last longer than the time $\frac{h}{E} = t$ determined by the condition that $t \, . \, E$ is of the same order as Planck's constant. Thus if two electrons are near each other, although neither of them can emit a photon according to the conservation of energy and momentum, it is possible for one of them to emit a photon which the other one immediately absorbs. The effect of this is to produce an interaction between the electrons, and this interaction is, in fact, the one which is measured as the ordinary electrical inverse square law repulsion between them. A process which occurs in this way with a temporary breaking of the rule of conservation of energy is called virtual, and so we have a diagram for the electron interaction by means of virtual photon exchange in the form of *Figure 42,* or in the form of an equation

$$e, e \leftrightarrow e, e.$$

Here, of course, the real particles are all represented by open-ended lines, that is they come from outside and they go off to outside again, but the virtual photon has both its ends tied up with other particles, so that there is never actually any opportunity for observing it. All of these interactions could equally well go the other way, and this is the principle of reversability in time, which is also a fundamental one in quantum mechanics, that is to say that an electron can similarly absorb a photon, although only at the expense of breaking energy conservation.

There is also another principle which is rather closely related to this idea that the time can be reversed. This other principle is that to

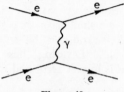

Figure 42

every particle there corresponds a similar anti-particle. If the orginal particle is charged, the anti-particle has opposite charge, but there are also anti-particles corresponding to neutral particles. We have already spoken about the anti-particles to the electron and the proton, that is the positron and the anti-proton. It can happen that in the case of neutral particles the anti-particle can be the same as the original particle, but this fact need not concern us here. How are the anti-particles coupled together, and how do they react with the original particles? The way of introducing them is extremely

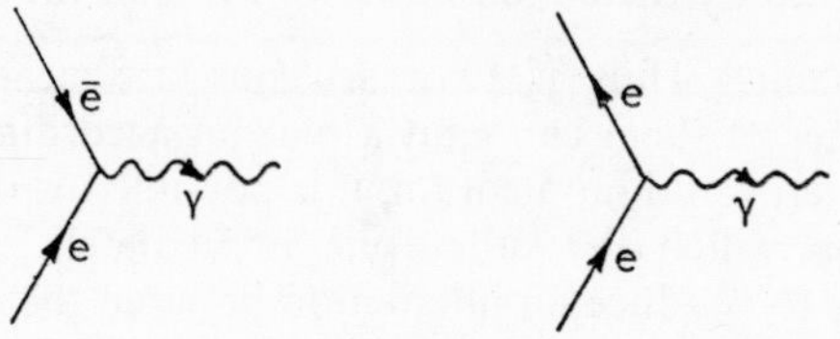

Figure 43

simple—we merely have to reverse the arrow on the track of one of the particles and we have the anti-particle, just as we explained in the particular classical case earlier on. Corresponding to the original diagram in which an electron emitted a photon and then continued as an electron, we would have a diagram in which an electron and a positron joined together and emit a photon. The rule is more easily seen if we have something in the form of an equation where we have e becoming e, γ and the new process is one where e, $\bar{e}$ becomes γ, $\bar{e}$ representing the positron or anti-electron. The rule, then, is simply that one can take a particle from one side of an equation and put it on the other side, if we at the same time turn it into its anti-particle (*Figure 43*). What happens if instead of transferring the electron to the other side we transfer the photon? We find that we get something which only differs from our previous equation by the direction of the arrow, that is by time reversal, a fact which corresponds to the known fact that the photon has as its anti-particle the same particle—the photon is its own anti-particle. Any particles which can couple together by exchange of photons are said to be charged and this coupling is called the electro-magnetic coupling.

Parity Non-conservation

There are, however, other couplings which arise, some of them weaker than the electro-magnetic, and some of them stronger. One which is about a thousand times weaker than the electro-magnetic is that which is postulated to account for the decay of nuclei. For example, the neutron, which is the neutral particle like the proton, decays after about a thousand seconds into a proton, an electron, and the anti-particle to a neutrino. (This is a particle very much like the neutrino in properties, but only to be distinguished from a neutrino by the fact that it is not identical with it.) We could look on this decay as the direct result of a coupling between the neutron, the proton, the neutrino and electron. Another example of such a decay is that of the μ-meson, which decays to an electron, a neutrino and an anti-neutrino. Both of these interactions involve neutrinos, and they also have something else in common which caused a great deal of discussion and surprise when it was first discovered. That is, these are interactions which violate the reflection symmetry, sometimes known as the law of conservation of parity.

It was for a long time thought that corresponding to any physical process it was possible for the mirror image process also to exist. That is to say, that the distinction between a right and a left-handed glove was only one which was relative, not that some kinds of gloves were intrinsically left-handed and others definitely right-handed, but just that there were these two kinds of gloves, both of them existing. In early 1957 experiments were made at the suggestion of Yang and Lee which showed that this principle was not in fact true. In these experiments, which were carried out at very low temperatures, electrons were emitted from cobalt-60, and it turned out that the electrons came out more in a certain direction than would be expected if the mirror image experiment were also a possibility. That is to say that, in the experiment as actually carried out, the electrons came out in a certain direction, but the mirror image experiment would give them orientated in an opposite direction. It appeared that, since this mirror image experiment could not exist, there was an absolute difference between right and left. However, if the cobalt-60 were replaced by anti-cobalt 60, and positrons were emitted, then, as far as we know, the opposite orientation of things would arise, so that the mirror image is still a possible experiment provided that all the particles are changed into anti-particles.

While we are mentioning various kinds of couplings between particles we ought also to mention the gravitational coupling, but this is so very much weaker than the electro-magnetic, 10^{39} times weaker, that it is always neglected in quantum field theory.

Strong Coupling

Besides all these couplings which are all weak, there is the coupling which holds together the particles in the nucleus, and this must be very much stronger. The strong couplings, and the particles which show strong coupling, are the ones which we want to discuss in the rest of this book. The electron, the μ-meson and the neutrino do not have strong couplings to any particle. The K meson, of the kind discovered by Leprince-Ringuet, and heavier particles like the neutron and the proton, are strongly interacting.

The way of studying the forces in the nucleus is principally by scattering neutrons and protons by protons. The forces concerned are very different from the inverse square law force of gravitation. Such a force, as we know, is very large near to the source, and it falls off steadily all the way outwards. In this case the nuclear force consists of a very strong repulsive force at very short distances, and then an attractive force at rather larger distances, which falls rapidly to zero when we get beyond the limit of nuclear forces at a distance of about 10^{-13} cms. The whole situation is a little more complicated than this, as it depends on the orientation of the proton and the neutron in a rather complicated way, and also on their velocities. But if we neglect even these, the remaining situation is quite a complicated one. However, it is not quite so bad as it might be, for the force between two protons, and that between a proton and a neutron, and that between two neutrons all seem to be equal. This is, of course, neglecting the electrical forces between the protons, which do not arise in the other cases, but these are very small compared with the nuclear field, and if we allow for these then there is very close equality between the remaining forces in the three cases. That means that there is some sort of symmetry, so that it does not really matter, so far as the nuclear forces are concerned, whether a particle is a proton or a neutron. This is a situation which arises with other strongly interacting particles—they come in sets. Here we have a set of two, the proton and neutron, which can, for the purposes of the nuclear forces, be regarded as two different states of a single particle. The two states are, for certain historical reasons, called two states of isotopic spin, and, because there are two states here, the physicists say that the combined proton-neutron particle, which is called a nucleon, has isotopic spin $\frac{1}{2}$. It is not necessary for our purposes to explain why such a curious notation should be employed, but it will suffice to say that it is not arbitrary, and that the way of specifying an isotopic spin expresses fairly accurately the way in which these sets of particles come. Moreover, as far as strong interactions are concerned, it is found that the total isotopic spin of the particles which enter is conserved. But this conservation does not apply to weak interactions like electrodynamics. This has some effect when we try to incorporate Yukawa's idea of the nuclear forces being the result of a particle (meson) being exchanged between the protons and the neutrons.

Let us consider a process like the one described for the electron being emitted from an excited atom, in which a proton becomes a neutron, and some other particle. This other particle will of course have to carry away the positive charge which is on the proton, and we shall use the letter π for it, because it is in fact a π-meson.

Now if we have a proton and a neutron close together there will be a force between them because of the transfer of a π-meson between them. The situation here is not quite like the electron situation, because there is no need for the π-meson to be virtual. If we set down the equations for conservation of energy and momentum and suppose that m_0 is the rest mass of the proton, we can consider the situation according to an observer with respect to whom the proton is at rest, and then the energy E_1 of the π-meson and the energy E_2 of the neutron, and their respective momenta p_1 and p_2 will satisfy the equations

$$E_1 + E_2 = m_0, \qquad p_1 + p_2 = 0,$$
$$E_1^2 - p_1^2 = m_\pi^2, \qquad E_2^2 - p_2^2 = m_0^2$$

from which we derive the results that E_1 is $m_\pi^2/2m_0$ and the corresponding expression for E_2. There is now no difficulty, so long as the mass of the π-meson is not zero. But although the transfer of the π-meson between the proton and the neutron need not be virtual, and indeed one can observe π-mesons produced in such a way, it *can* also be virtual, that is to say it can exist for a very short time. This transfer is what is known as an exchange force, because when it happens the proton becomes a neutron, and the neutron becomes a proton. This would give us a force between a proton and a neutron. However, this cannot be the whole story, because there must be an identical force between two protons and between two neutrons, and the only way in which two protons could interact in this way would be by exchanging a neutral particle; the same goes for two neutrons. There must therefore be a neutral particle very much like the π-meson, and this is the neutral π-meson. This will make a slight difference to the exchange force between the neutron and proton, because the possibility of exchanging a neutral π-meson would give a non-exchange part to the force. It then turns out to be possible to arrange the amplitude with which these various interactions take place in such a way that there is indeed the required symmetry between nuclear forces.

Strange Particles

Now there are other particles which are also strongly coupled to π-mesons and to nucleons. These new particles were first discovered in cosmic rays. The most striking one, and in many ways the most important, is the one which is now called by the letter Λ, a neutral particle which decays into a proton and a negative π-meson after about 10^{-10} seconds. The mass of this is considerably more than the proton; indeed it is about 2182 electron masses compared with 1836 for the proton. It seems as if the interaction time, 10^{-10} seconds, is very short, and so it is by everyday standards. But it happens that, from the strength of the strong interaction, we can get an estimate of the kind of times which we would expect to occur here, and these are very much shorter, about 10^{-23} seconds. So that in fact these particles are living very much longer than we would expect. The conclusion drawn from this is that the decay in question is really a weak interaction, so that there is no such strong coupling as would connect Λ with proton and π-meson. But, if this is so, then it is very difficult to know how the Λ-particles could be produced, for the cosmic rays are made up of protons which hit nuclei containing protons and neutrons, and of course virtual π-mesons because of the strong coupling. Now in such an interaction we know that the Λ's are produced very copiously, but the interaction concerned cannot simply be that the p and π gives Λ, for this is not a strong interaction. It is no good bringing in something like a neutron and saying that the proton plus neutron gives Λ plus proton, for if this were so, then we could take the extra proton to the other side as an anti-proton, and we would then have a strong interaction of Λ becoming proton plus neutron plus anti-proton. We know that the anti-proton and the neutron strongly interact to give a π-meson, so that this interaction would be strong. In the same way we cannot derive the Λ from three neutrons, because although the original interaction of the Λ and the p is a weak one it still does exist and so there would be the possibility of the three neutrons of the nucleus turning to one through a virtual reaction, and this could release a large amount of energy, the mass of two neutrons. Then no nucleus except that of hydrogen could possibly be stable.

TABLE OF ELEMENTARY PARTICLES IN 1961

Name	Symbol	Mass (electron masses)	Life time (secs)	Common decay mode
Photon	γ	0	Stable	
Neutrino	ν	0	Stable	
Electron	e	1	Stable	
μ-meson	μ	206	10^{-6}	$e + \nu + \bar{\nu}$
Charged π-meson	$\pi^{\pm}$	273	10^{-8}	$\mu^{\pm} + \nu + \bar{\nu}$
Neutral π-meson	π^0	264	10^{-16}	2γ
Charged K-meson	k^+	966	10^{-8}	$\mu^+ + \nu$ ($\pi^+ + \pi^0$ also common)
Neutral K-meson	k^0	975	$\begin{cases} 10^{-10} \\ 10^{-8} \end{cases}$	$\pi^+ + \pi^-$ $\mu^{\pm} + \pi^{\pm} + (\nu$ or $\bar{\nu})$
Proton	p	1836	Stable	
Neutron	n	1838	1000	$p + e + \nu$
Λ-meson	Λ	2183	10^{-10}	$p + \pi^-$ ($n + \pi^0$ also common)
Positive Σ-meson	Σ^+	2329	10^{-10}	$p + \pi^0$ ($n + \pi^+$ also common)
Neutral Σ-meson	Σ^0	2333 (?)	10^{-11}	$\Lambda + \gamma$
Negative Σ-meson	Σ^-	2342	10^{-10}	$n + \pi^-$
Neutral cascade particles	Ξ^0	2566	10^{-10}	$\Lambda + \pi^0$
Negative cascade	Ξ^-	2581	10^{-10}	$\Lambda + \pi^-$

On the other hand we know that matter in general is extraordinarily stable. Experiments have been done to try to detect disintegrations, and we now know that the nuclei which we commonly call stable last for at least 10^{17} years. The way out of this difficulty which was found was that, in the strong productions, more than one of these particles must be produced at once. For example, two neutrons could give us two Λ particles. These particles like the K-particles and other strongly interacting ones have properties which puzzled physicists very much at the time when they were first found, and indeed still puzzle them to a certain extent, and for this reason they are often called strange particles. In fact the first strange particle to be found was the one which we mentioned earlier, discovered by Leprince-Ringuet in cosmic ray photographs, the K-meson which decays into π-mesons. The neutral K-meson decays into π-mesons of opposite signs in about 10^{-10} seconds. This presents exactly the same problem as the decay of the Λ-particle. The conclusion come to was, that the two particles must be produced together so that the real production was the result of a strong coupling in which a neutron became a Λ-particle and a K-meson. Experiment has in fact shown that these particles are produced together in nuclear collisions. Actually the Λ is the lightest of a whole set of particles which are shown in the Table on page 101, which have since been discovered with properties somewhat similar to the Λ-particle, but whereas the Λ-particle, so far as we know, is always neutral, the new particles can also have various charges. They all interact strongly in the way that we have been speaking of.

In this chapter we have tried to give a summary of the recent experimental situation in elementary particle physics, because unless we have a general understanding of this situation without necessarily understanding how each of the experiments are carried out, we cannot appreciate the particular simplifications which our idea of an environment has made in the particular theory of strong interactions which will be considered in the next chapter. The discussions which we have given in this chapter have been mostly of experimental evidence, and have not advanced our discussion of the environment at all. In the next chapter we will take up this discussion again and try to find a way of looking at these things which is more in keeping with the discussions of relativity which have gone before. When we do this we shall be able to show how this leads to a new extension of the concept of observing a particle, which has resulted in a great increase in the number of elementary particles known.

CHAPTER 7

COLLISION PROCESSES

The Scattering Amplitude

The treatment by quantum field theory of the various interactions, which was discussed in the last chapter, has not been very successful. So far as the interaction of the lighter particles, especially electrons with the electro-magnetic field is concerned, a great deal has been done. But when we consider the association between fields, and the heavy, strongly interacting particles, we find that field theory has really made no progress at all. What appears to be progress is really attempts to describe things in a qualitative fashion, but without any close agreement with the experiments.

It is natural therefore to try to describe these things in a different way with new ideas which come from the ones we have already, that is, from field theory, but with the actual description taking a different form and in many ways much more simple one. We are concerned with particles about which all our information comes from collision processes. Here two particles meet each other and a reaction takes place which we do not understand at all, and as a result two new particles come out. The region in which the interaction takes place is very small, and about this interaction we wish to say nothing, except which particles go in and which come out. The actual experimental data is described in a rather complicated manner in terms of what is called scattering cross-section. This is a way of associating numbers with the process which tells us something about the effect of a large number of such processes happening at once. It tells us the chance of particles of a certain kind being produced in a certain direction. The actual details of the scattering cross-section, and so on, are all rather technical, and need not be elaborated here. All that we need to know for our purposes is that a certain number can be associated with the process, and this number must of course depend upon the energies and momenta of the incoming and outgoing particles.

Now let us see what general remarks can be made about the dependence of the scattering cross-section on the incoming and outgoing particles. Reactions involve various numbers of particles, but the most typical number to choose is 4, two going in and two going out. It is true that one can have fewer (three is not uncommon) and one can have more, but the case of three particles is rather simple, and when the case of four has been considered, the reader will easily be able to consider the case of three for himself. The case of five or more particles has not yet been fully analysed, but there is every confidence that the methods employed so far will work for larger numbers, if only they can be carried out. The main thing here is not to stress too much which particles go in and which come out; after all, an ingoing particle could always be replaced by the corresponding outgoing anti-particle, so that there is no hard and fast distinction between the ingoing and outgoing particles. In fact, we wish to consider a number of cases together, in some of which a particle goes in and in others a corresponding anti-particle comes out. For

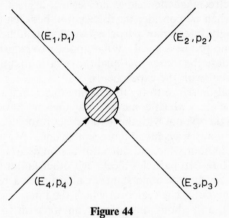

Figure 44

this reason we may as well consider the impossible (or at least highly unlikely) reaction which consists of four particles all coming in. This has the advantage that all four particles are treated on exactly the same footing. We shall know, in fact, that two of these particles must in fact be replaced by their anti-particles coming out, but which two these are we leave undetermined for the moment (*Figure 44*). Each of these particles has an incoming energy and an incoming momentum, and we can call the energies E_1, E_2, E_3, and E_4 and the momenta p_1, p_2, p_3, and p_4. In this rather amazing process in which apparently four particles come in and totally disappear it is clear that there will be no energy and no momentum left at the end, so that the sum of the four E's and the sum of the four p's must both be zero. This is really a symmetrical way of expressing the conservation of momentum in the collision process. Now associated with the four particles by means of their energy and momentum are some invariant quantities, that is numbers that will be the same for all observers. The energy and the momentum as we know, are not, but for each particle $E^2 - p^2$ is invariant, because it is the rest mass

of that particle. These rest masses we shall suppose known and so
no great interest attaches to those four invariants. But there are
another three invariants of the system which are of interest, and these
arise in the following way.

The Invariants

We have deduced the invariants $E^2 - p^2$ for a particle from the
fact that it is actually equal to the rest mass, but we could equally
well have worked out the way in which E and p are transformed by
Lorentz transformation from one observer to another, and we should
then obviously have found that $E^2 - p^2$ was a quantity which was not
changed by the Lorentz transformation. Now the Lorentz transformations are *linear* in the sense that if we add together two energies
and two momenta corresponding to two particles, and then transform the result, we shall get an energy and momentum which is the
same as if we were to transform the energies and momenta of the two
particles first and then add the result afterwards. As a consequence
of this it is clear that, for instance, $s_1 = (E_1 + E_4)^2 - (p_1 + p_4)^2$
is an invariant quantity, and so also are

$$s_2 = (E_2 + E_4)^2 - (p_2 + p_4)^2, \quad s_3 = (E_3 + E_4)^2 - (p_3 + p_4)^2.$$

Each of these quantities is, in fact, equal to another one, which we
could write down by using the fact that the sum of all the E's and all
the p's is zero. Here we must remember that the momenta have
direction as well as magnitude, and so $p_1 + p_4$ is a convenient
shorthand for the momentum that results by applying both p_1 and
p_4—a momentum which is obviously determined as the third side
of a triangle with p_1 and p_4 represented (in magnitude and direction)
by a pair of adjacent sides. These three invariants are of great
importance in determining scattering. Any calculation of the
scattering cross-section must be carried out in terms of the invariants
of the system, since it cannot depend upon the particular observer
with respect to whom the motion of the particles are being described.
Now it is, as a matter of fact, the case that only these three invariants
exist for the system apart, of course, from the four rest masses which
we had originally. In order to see this we must imagine a particular
choice of reference frame in which one of the particles is at rest so
that its momentum vector is zero, and it has only an energy which
is its rest mass. The other three then have momentum vectors, and
it is a well-known fact that, apart from the lengths of these momentum vectors, there are only three invariants for this system corresponding, say, to the angle between these three momenta. There are
three momenta and so three angles between them, and when we
have given these three angles and the size of the momenta we have

5

defined the three momenta completely except that the whole set of them could be swung round to a different position. There will then be exactly three invariants of this kind for the three momenta. Since this is the situation in the particular reference frame which we have chosen with one of the particles at rest, it will be the case in general that there are exactly three invariants, so long as we suppose that the rest masses and energies are known.

Now these three invariants which we have found here must therefore be the only invariants of the system which can enter into the expression for the scattering cross-section. However, not all of these invariants are independent of each other, for we notice at once that $s_1 + s_2 + s_3$ is the sum of the squares of the four rest masses, so that only two of the variables, say s_1 and s_2 need be given and the third one is then determined. There are then *two* independent invariants from which the scattering cross-section has to be determined.

The Three Possible Channels

Now let us consider a little more carefully what happens when we take into account that some of the particles are going in and others are coming out. Let us first take the case where the particles P_1 and P_2 are going in, and particles P_3 and P_4 are coming out, and the four particles are all of equal mass. Let us adopt, moreover, such a reference frame that the total momentum of the particles coming in beforehand is 0. This is known as the centre-of-mass system. Then the energy and momentum of the first particle being E_1 and p_1, those for the second particle must be E_1 and $-p_1$. Similarly the two energies for the third and fourth particles must be equal to each other but since these are anti-particles the corresponding energies will be negative, and in fact these two energies, in order to make the sum of the four E's zero will both be $-E_1$. Then the corresponding momenta for the other two particles will have to be p_3 and $-p_3$ where p_3 is the momentum of the particle, which has the same size as p_1, because $E_1^2 - p_1^2$ is the rest mass, and $E_3^2 - p_3^2$ is also the rest mass, and we are assuming the special case in which all four of the rest masses are equal. Naturally p_3 will, in general, be in a different direction from p_1. Now when we come to work out the values of the three invariants we find that s_1 and s_2 are both negative, but s_3 is $4E_1^2$. That is to say that the particular case where the particles p_3 and p_4 are going out is characterised by the third invariant being positive and indeed greater than $4M^2$, and the other two being necessarily negative. The other cases which we might consider are when p_1 and p_4 and p_2 and p_4 are coming out, and these are called respectively channel 1 and channel 2, the case which we have just analysed at length being channel 3. A good way of representing the situation is to draw a triangle ABC and measure the invariants from the sides of the triangle, s_1 being measured upwards from the side BC, s_2 from the side CA and s_3 from the side AB. Let us choose the units of measurement in such a way that the quantity $4M^2$ is the amount that the vertices of the triangle are each distant from the opposite sides, and then it will at once be clear in the figure (*Figure*

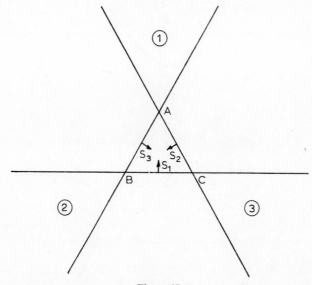

Figure 45

45) that the regions for each of the three channels in which the motion can subsist are those of the planes which are cut off by the prolongation of the sides of the triangle and are marked as 1, 2 and 3 in the diagram. This analysis supposes that all the masses have the same value, and it is a little more complicated to carry out the corresponding analysis when the masses have different values, but the effect is not very different.

We can see in the next diagram (*Figure 46*) what the situation is when the masses have all different values. The interesting thing about the diagram in the case when the masses are different is that not only are there the three regions of very much the same shape as before, except that the boundaries are curves instead of straight lines, but there is also a region in the centre which did not exist before. This region in the centre can only be there if one of the masses is greater than the sum of the other three, and it is found that it corresponds to the case when one particle decays into three others, so that a single particle enters and three come out, instead of two entering and two coming out. This is not possible, of course, if all the masses are equal, which is why our analysis did not give this possibility previously. The position which we have reached then is this: in our diagram there are certain regions, which are called the physical regions for the three channels, and there are certain

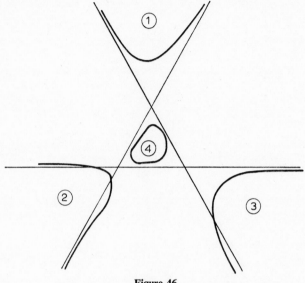

Figure 46

un-physical regions, and the two variables in terms of which we have to express the scattering amplitude have certain ranges of values in these physical regions.

The Symmetry between Particle and Environment

We shall now state what is sometimes called the substitution law, which is a statement about the form that the scattering amplitude (which determines the cross-section) can have when it is described in terms of these three invariants. What one wants to say about it is that it does not matter which particles come in and which go out. The fact that this should be so is an empirical law, which has been verified by a large number of scattering experiments with heavy particles, and it turns out that fully to express this empirical law in terms of mathematics is to assume a very great deal of information. What this law really means in terms of our way of looking at things in this book is this: the environment in which an elementary particle finds itself does not depend at all on such things as gravitational fields, and so on. All our information here comes by collision processes and the whole environment for such a process is *the other elementary particle concerned*. The substitution law now says that there is symmetry between particle and environment. The expression of this law in precise terms is, however, not so easy.

What we want to say is that the scattering amplitude is the same whether particles are going in or out, but of course this statement cannot be quite correct as it stands, because if particles are going in they have certain momenta, and if they are coming out they may have certain different momenta, the scattering amplitude depending on the momenta by means of the invariants. Whether the particles are coming in or coming out is simply a question of what range of possibilities is open to the various invariants, in particular to any two of them, say, s_1 and s_2, which together must be enough to determine the scattering amplitude. So that we really wish to say that the scattering amplitude depends on the two invariants *in exactly the same way* for channel 1 as for channel 2 and for channel 3. Although this sounds very plausible we find that we are immediately up against a very serious mathematical difficulty. The scattering amplitude depends on the values of the invariants, or as one expresses it mathematically, it is a function of the values of the invariants. And these invariants can have their values in different ranges, so that what we are trying to say here is that a certain function is the *same* function of two variables, and it is the same function whether the variables are in one range or another range. To see the nature of this trouble it will be simpler to start by considering functions of one variable to see what sort of difficulty arises there.

Singularities of Functions

In the first place we know that if we specify the value of a function of x, say $f(x)$, between the values 0 and 1 of x we have specified absolutely nothing at all about its value for other ranges of x, say for $x = -1$ to 0. But this fact, serious as it is for our purposes, should perhaps not be taken too seriously, for the kind of functions which we are accustomed to dealing with in physics have various nice properties of continuity and so on, and if we say that the values of $f(x)$ for x not in the range (0, 1) are completely arbitrary, the chances are that some of those properties of continuity and so on may be contradicted by this. The amount of arbitrariness open to us is therefore not quite so great as the pure mathematicians would have us believe. However, we cannot get out of things quite so simply. We could, if we wished, restrict ourselves, without losing a great deal of information, to functions which could be expressed either by an algebraic expression in x such as $f(x) = a + bx + cx^2$, or else by a power series in x. As an example of the latter kind of function we know that $\dfrac{1}{1-x}$ by successive division can be expressed in the form

$$\frac{1}{1-x} = 1 + x + x^2 + \ldots$$

The latter piece of manipulation is, however, only valid if we can properly give meaning to the right-hand side of the equation, that is to the infinite series. We have written it with plus signs, so that it looks as though an ordinary sum is in question here, but this cannot really be the case, and the infinite series must be given a meaning in a new way, because we cannot simply sit down and add up all the terms. When we say that an infinite series has a certain sum this is simply a convention by which we mean that by taking sufficiently many terms of the series we can get as near to the sum as we wish. This is indeed the case here, so long as x has a suitable value, because it is easy to show, again by successive division, that the sum of n terms of the series $1 + x + x^2 + \ldots$, and so on, is $\dfrac{1 - x^n}{1 - x}$. The remainder, which is the discrepancy between the function which we were setting out to represent and the actual series is $\dfrac{x^n}{1 - x}$ and so long as x is smaller in absolute value than 1, that is to say so long as x lies between -1 and 1, this remainder can be made as small as we wish by taking n sufficiently large, i.e. by taking sufficient terms of the series. Thus, to seek a power series expression for the function $\dfrac{1}{1-x}$ is perfectly all right so long as x lies between -1 and 1. The difficulty arises when we want to have a power series expansion, or some other such expansion, for a function outside the range in which the obvious one is available. In this case, of course, we know that the function for any values of x is $\dfrac{1}{1-x}$ and so we do not really need an expansion, but we are supposing that we may have a function for which this simple finite form is not available and we have only the power series to go on. We must ask ourselves, then, why it is that the power series which we are getting only determines the function over a certain region of values of x. Part of the answer is at once obvious. When we approach the point $x = 1$, there is a singularity of the function; that is to say, the function itself is not defined at all for the value $x = 1$, but by choosing x arbitrarily near to 1 we can make the function as large as we please. When something like this is happening it is, of course, not at all surprising that the series representing the function should run into trouble at that point.

Difficulties away from Singularities

But this is, as we have said, only half an answer, for it explains why the series runs into trouble at $x = 1$, but it does not at all explain why it runs into trouble at $x = -1$. It is true, of course, that the trouble at $x = -1$ is not quite so serious as the trouble at $x = 1$. We could, for instance, adopt a slight further convention for summing the series there, for it has the form $1 - 1 + 1 - 1 + \ldots$ and so on, and there is a well-known method for assigning a sum to a series which strictly speaking does not have one. In this method we take successive averages of the partial sums; that is to say, if we write s_n for the sum of the first n terms, then we consider in succession $s_1, \dfrac{s_1 + s_2}{2}, \dfrac{s_1 + s_2 + s_3}{3}, \ldots$ and so on, and if this sequence of numbers becomes nearer and nearer to some particular number we assign that as a conventional sum of the series. If we employ this device here we would get the value $\frac{1}{2}$ for the sum of the series, which is indeed the value for $\dfrac{1}{1 - x}$ when x is -1. But this is rather a device which happens to give the "right" answer in this particular case; we have no confidence that it would in other cases. Strictly speaking, we should say that the point $x = -1$ is a difficult point for the series, just like the point $x = 1$. We notice that a partial explanation of the difficulty at $x = -1$ is occasioned by the fact that the variable in the series expansion is x itself, that is to say that $x = 0$ is the *centre* of the range in which the expansion is valid. Another way of looking at this is to say that we are expanding about the point $x = 0$, that there is a singularity at $x = 1$, and that this leads to another difficulty at the reflection $x = -1$, the image-point of the first singularity in the point $x = 0$ about which we are expanding. This will be an explanation if the range of validity of a power series expansion about a certain point is symmetrical about that point. For example, we could find an expansion of $\dfrac{1}{1 - x}$ outside the range of x between -1 and 1, for we could write $\dfrac{1}{1 - x}$ as $\dfrac{-1}{1 + (x - 2)}$, and then we can expand this in powers of $x - 2$ by repeated division in the same way. This new series will have a meaning and it will signify the function we wish it to signify so long as $x - 2$ lies in the range between -1 and 1, that is so long as x lies between 1 and 3, and here again the two points of difficulty at which the expansion breaks down, 1 and 3, are equidistant from the point $x = 2$ which is the point about which we are expanding. It is not completely clear at the moment why there should be this symmetry in the two singularities of the series with respect to the point at which the expansion takes place, but we need not go into this more fully here because it will become clear later why this must be so.

Functions without Singularities

But this explanation which we have given of the breakdown of the series for $\dfrac{1}{1 - x}$ does not help at all with more complicated functions. Consider, for instance, the function $\dfrac{1}{1 + x^2}$ which by repeated division we can again evaluate as $1 - x^2 + x^4 - \ldots$ etc. Here we have a series which it is easy to see means what we wish it to mean so long as x is less than 1 and greater than -1. Indeed, by the same argument as before, if x has any value, then the sum of n terms of the series is easily found to be

$$\frac{1 - (-x)^{2n}}{1 + x^2},$$

and this will be as near as we wish to $\dfrac{1}{1 + x^2}$, so long as x lies between -1 and 1. But if x is equal to -1 or 1 we again have a series to which we can perhaps conventionally attach the sum $\frac{1}{2}$, but here again it is only a convention, and we ought really to say that at -1 and 1 the expansion breaks down. The fact that there is a device which enables us to attach a conventional sum at -1 and 1 is of no importance because, even if we are able to save the series at that point, it certainly breaks down as soon as x is greater than 1 or less than -1. And yet the original function had no singularity of any kind at 1 or -1 but in fact simply has the value $\frac{1}{2}$ there! Thus it is clear that there is some other effect which is causing the expansion of the series to break down, and which is not clearly exhibited in the form of the function.

Irrational Numbers

It may perhaps help here if we take a simpler case which might have arisen had the Greek geometers known about infinite series. Instead of taking $\dfrac{1}{1 + x^2}$, let us consider $\dfrac{1}{2 - x^2}$ with this difference, that, instead of taking x to be any number, let us just suppose that we are working always in the set of rational numbers, that is numbers which can be expressed in the form p/q where p and q are integers. The reason for the reference to Greek geometers was because, until the discovery that the diagonal of a square had a magnitude which was not rational in terms of the sides, they supposed that all the magnitudes which entered were rationals, and the discovery of the irrationality of the diagonal of the square, that is to say that $\sqrt{2}$ could not be expressed as a rational number, was a severe shock to them.

If we then consider the expansion of $\dfrac{1}{2-x^2}$ in the same way we find easily enough

$$\frac{1}{2-x^2} = \frac{1}{2} + \frac{1}{4}x^2 + \frac{1}{8}x^4 + \ldots,$$

so long as x^2 is less than 2. If x^2 is greater than 2 there certainly is no possibility of the series expressing the function, and if $x^2 = 2$ the same is true, unless we adopt some rather artificial convention about assigning a sum to the series. Thus we can say that the function is represented by the series so long as x^2 is less than 2 and is not represented by it when x^2 is greater than 2. Nowadays we would say that the trouble is that the function itself has singularities at the points $x = \pm\sqrt{2}$, but if we were working with the rational numbers only we could not say that there was a singularity for any particular rational number, we should just have to say that the series broke down between the x's whose squares were less than 2 and the x's whose squares were greater than two, and so we should have a difficulty of very much the same sort as we have just had with $\dfrac{1}{1+x^2}$, that the series broke down although so far as we could see there was no singularity of the function.

One way out of this, without calling in the whole theory of real numbers, would be to take the set of rational numbers which we have been dealing with, and adjoin to it one number, which is not rational, which we could define as the root of the equation $x^2 - 2 = 0$. If we call this number k then any number of our new set will be of the form $a + bk$ where a and b are rationals, and we shall define addition and multiplication of these numbers in exactly the same way as with rationals, that is to say

$$(a + bk) + (c + dk) = a + c + k(b + d),$$
$$(a + bk)(c + dk) = ac + 2bd + k(bc + ad).$$

We should find that we could deal with these numbers in exactly the same way as we could with the rationals; that is, we could add, subtract, multiply and divide by them, unless one of them were zero, in which case division would be impossible.

We could describe this procedure in more colloquial terms by saying that we had added to the set of rational numbers the square root of 2, but if anyone were still imbued with the spirit of having all the numbers rational, then we could avoid offending his suscepti-bilities by saying instead that we adjoined a number which was a root of a certain equation. He would not then be able to say "you have adjoined the square root of 2 but it does not exist", because we could certainly perform this construction so long as we give him all the rules for manipulating the numbers which we have con-structed; it just happens that these rules are very conveniently summarised by saying that the quantity k which we have introduced is to be manipulated as if it were the square root of 2. This example is useful to us because we all know nowadays how to deal with the square root 2; we simply use decimal expansions of numbers, and then we can express all square roots.

Imaginary Numbers

Let us see if we can learn a lesson from this for our function $\dfrac{1}{1 + x^2}$. What we did in the case of the square root of 2 was to adjoin a number which made the denominator vanish, and thus we adjoined to our set of numbers the singularities of the function which were not previously in the set. Here then we should adjoin to the set of real numbers the solution of the equation $x^2 + 1 = 0$. In the same way as before, any objector who contended that this was a non-existent number could be silenced by pointing out that this construction was certainly possible so long as he was given all the rules for carrying it out. The symbol used for the root of the equation $x^2 + 1 = 0$ is always i and then any number of the new set will have the form $a + ib$, and the rules for addition and multiplication will be as follows

$$(a + ib) + (c + id) = a + c + i(b + d),$$
$$(a + ib)(c + id) = ac - bd + i(bc + ad),$$

where, of course, these rules are easily remembered simply by treat-ing i as if it were an ordinary number whose square was -1. The corresponding set of numbers which we derive in this way is called the set of complex numbers. These complex numbers have been used in mathematics for many years, but in many discussions a certain air of mystery still attaches to them, although it is hard to see exactly why. When we introduce the set of complex numbers there is certainly no difficulty about the function, because we can see certain singularities in it. $\dfrac{1}{1 + x^2}$ has a singularity at $x = i$, and, of course, another one at $x = -i$. How shall we represent this on our Figure? We have represented numbers by measurements along a line, and so this suggests that we should represent the numbers $a + ib$, where a and b are both real numbers, by measurements in a

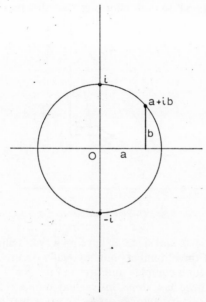

Figure 47

plane. There is of course no necessity to do this, neither does it have any mystical significance; it is simply a convenient way of representing the numbers. If we do represent the number $a + ib$ by a point on the plane whose distance along one line is a and then whose distance at right-angles to it is b (*Figure 47*) then the singularities will be at the points i and $-i$, unit distance up and down the vertical axis. Now the question is: for what points in the plane will a certain series mean the function which we wish it to mean? Or, at any rate, for what points will a certain series have a definite sum assigned to it, according to our rule for assigning a sum to an infinite series? A more brief way of putting this is to ask for what points in the plane does the infinite series *converge*? Convergence is simply the requirement on a series that a sum can be attached to it. In order to establish the region in which an infinite series of the form which we have been considering converges, we have to work out a little of the theory of these complex numbers.

The Circle of Convergence

Firstly, to any complex number $a + ib$ there corresponds another one which is intimately associated with it, that is $a - ib$. The reason for the close connection between these two numbers is that they just correspond to our choosing two different roots of the

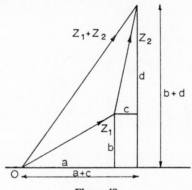

Figure 48

equation $x^2 + 1 = 0$, and since we have no way of telling which root is which, each of these numbers might equally occur. The notation z is usually used for a complex number, and if z is $a + ib$ we write $\bar{z}$ for $a - ib$. When we have done this we find at once that the product $z\bar{z}$ is in fact an ordinary number, or as we say a real number, being in fact $a^2 + b^2$. $a^2 + b^2$ is the square of the length of the distance from the origin to the point in the plane which we have chosen to represent the number. This magnitude is called the square of the modulus of the complex number, the modulus being the positive value of the square root. Now we have a result, which is very useful in the discussion of convergence, about the modulus of the sum of two complex numbers; in fact we can state at once that the modulus of $z_1 + z_2$ is less than or equal to the sum of the moduli of z_1 and z_2. This is because if we draw a diagram (*Figure 48*) to represent the addition of z_1 and z_2 we find that the complex number $z_1 + z_2$ is represented by a stroke from the origin which is the third side of a triangle of which strokes representing z_1 and z_2 are adjacent sides. So our statement is simply Euclid's well-known theorem that any two sides of a triangle are together greater than the third side. This result could obviously be extended to the sum of any number of complex numbers, and so we can straight away say something about the sum of a series.

If we have a series of complex terms, that is, if we consider an expansion like

$$a_0 + a_1 z + a_2 z^2 + a_3 z^3 + \ldots$$

where the various terms are complex (i.e. both the z is complex and also the coefficients of the powers of z), then the modulus of the sum of n terms of this series is less than or equal to the sum of the moduli. And this is a series of real terms. Therefore if this series of real terms converges, the corresponding series of complex terms will converge. Now the series of real terms converges, as we know, if $|z|$ lies in a certain interval symmetrical about the origin. Of course, as it is $|z|$ that we are concerned with, the negative values cannot actually arise, and we have a certain interval from the origin up to a certain value, R say. That is to say, the original series certainly converges at all points inside a region which consists of all those points whose distance from the origin is less than R. The region in question is therefore in our diagram a circle, whose centre is the origin. It can be shown, but it does not concern us here particularly, that at points on the circle the series may or may not converge, but there are always some points on the circle at which it does not. The circle in question then is called the circle of convergence of the function, and since there are points on the circle at which it does not converge, but it converges everywhere inside the circle, we can see at once how to draw the circle of convergence for an expansion of the function about any particular point. That is, we draw a circle, centre that point, passing through the nearest singularity of the function. In the case $\dfrac{1}{1 + z^2}$, the singularities are at a unit distance up and down the vertical axis, and a circle which passes through these singularities and whose centre is the origin, intersects the real axis at the points -1 and 1, and so we see at once why it is that the expansion of $\dfrac{1}{1 + x^2}$ is limited at those two points, although the function is perfectly regular there. In the same way, for the $\dfrac{1}{1 - x}$ expansion, the circle intersects the axis at 1 and -1, and so we see the reason for the trouble at $x = -1$.

Analytic Continuation

Now the introduction of the conplex numbers explains the existence of these singularities off the real axis, but it does much more than this. We remarked earlier, in the case of the function $\dfrac{1}{1-x}$, that by writing it in a different form we could find an expansion of it about the point $x = 2$ instead of about the point $x = 0$, but we have no way, as long as we deal only with ordinary numbers, of connecting these two expansions together. That is to say, given the two series, there is no sense in which these two series represent the same function. At first this sounds absurd, for, if we sum the two series,

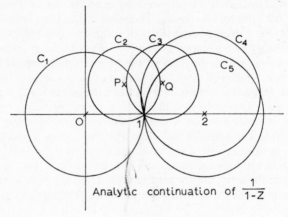

Analytic continuation of $\dfrac{1}{1-Z}$

Figure 49

we derive in each case the function $\dfrac{1}{1-x}$, but we cannot say, as long as x is an ordinary number, that we have the *same* function in each case, because the first series only gives us $\dfrac{1}{1-x}$ if x lies between -1 and 1, and the second series only gives us this sum if x lies between 1 and 3. The series are completely different functions, and we cannot assert any connection between them. Now once we are able to move about the whole plane, as it were, instead of along a line, the situation is completely different. The singularity at $x = 1$ was a barrier which prevented us ever getting from the region between -1 to 1 round to the other region which we were interested in, but when we can move about in the whole plane single points cease to be barriers and we can move around them. We start off (see *Figure 49*) expanding our function about $z = 0$ and we have a certain expansion which converges everywhere inside a circle C_1 of radius 1. Let us move then to some point P inside this circle, and let us work out how to expand the function about this new point instead of about the origin. This new point, P, will in general, of course, be a complex number, and if we expand the function about this complex point P we shall derive an expansion which is valid everywhere inside a circle C_2 passing through the nearest singularity. This nearest singularity is again $z = 1$ because that is the only singularity of the function. We therefore derive another circle through the point $z = 1$ which overlaps the first one but also goes outside it. By choosing a suitable point, Q, in this circle we can proceed to an expansion in yet another circle, C_3, which overlaps the second one but goes further on outside it, and so in this way we can arrive at an expansion which is valid in part of the region from $x = 1$ to $x = 3$, and in particular in the neighbourhood of $x = 2$. Then by expanding about $x = 2$ we derive the form of expansion which we had before, now valid in a circle C_5 centre $x = 2$, passing through $x = 1$. This process, which is known as analytic continuation, enables us to get from an expansion of a function valid in one range round to an expansion valid in another range. The reader may well wonder whether such a delightful process will always be possible; the answer is that it will not, for we can write down a series for which it is certainly impossible to get outside the unit circle. Such an example is provided by

$$f(z) = z^2 + z^4 + z^8 + z^{16} + \ldots$$

for which, clearly,

$$f(z) = z^2 + f(z^2).$$

Now $f(z)$ has obviously a singularity at $z = i$ since

$$f(i) = -1 + 1 + 1 + 1 \ldots$$

and since $f(z^2) = f(z) - z^2$, $f(z)$ has singularities at those of $f(z^2)$ i.e. $z^2 = i$, $z = \pm \sqrt{i}$. Repeating this process gives singularities all round the circle $|z| = 1$, as close together as we wish. The circle $|z| = 1$ for this function is what is known as a natural boundary of the function. However the functions which we shall usually be concerned with will not have natural boundaries, and the process of analytic continuation will be possible.

The Analytic Character of the Scattering Amplitude

Let us take stock now of the position. So long as we consider functions of complex variables, not of real variables, this process of analytic continuation is always possible and we can get around singularities. It then makes perfectly good sense in general to talk of two functions defined for instance by power series, each of which is valid only for certain ranges of the variables, as being the same function. What this means is that, if we start with one of the functions valid for a certain range of the variables, and we carry out the process of analytic continuation until we derive a function which is valid for the other range, we shall find that this is identical with the second of the functions in question. This provides us with an answer to the physical problem posed at the beginning of the chapter. In an elementary particle collision process, which is our sole source of information about the properties of elementary particles, there is complete symmetry between the particle and its environment, because these are simply two names for the two incoming particles. In order to express this fact we have to say that the scattering cross-section is the same function of the invariants no matter which channel is being considered. We broke off in our attempt to say this because, as we pointed out, it makes nonsense mathematically to speak of something being the same function of variables which have different ranges. Now there is one case known, and one only, in which such a statement does make sense, and that is when we have an analytic function of a complex variable. There *may* of course be other ways in which this sentence could make sense; there may be other kinds of functions for which this process of continuation can be carried out, but, if there are, we do not know them. For an analytic function of a complex variable however, the process of continuation can in general be carried out, and then it makes perfectly good sense to say that a function of a variable defined on some particular range of the variable is equal to another function of the variable defined on a different range.

Of course, the physical situation is a little more complicated because the variables in question are two in number instead of one, the scattering amplitude being a function of two of the invariants, say s_1 and s_2, s_3 being given in terms of those two. However, this is merely a technical matter which makes the mathematics more difficult but does not alter the conceptions in principle. In order to make our symmetry statement, then, what we have to do is to say that the scattering amplitude is an analytic function of the two invariants considered as complex variables. That is to say, we have to suppose that the energy and momentum variables which enter here can have complex variables as their values, although of course it is only real values of energy and momentum which have any significance physically. The complex values have to be introduced in order that we may be able to express the symmetry property, and then, in the complex planes of the two variables s_1 and s_2, we have to say that the scattering amplitude shall be an analytic function of these variables, for all the ranges allowed in the various channels. That is, it must be analytic in all three channels together, and this is actually a very severe restriction on the function indeed. There is a little more to it than this, for any analytic function must have singularities somewhere, although "somewhere" in this statement, must be taken to include the possibility that it is at infinity, for if a function has no singularities anywhere, including infinity, this means that the series must converge everywhere. If this is so it is easy to see that every coefficient of the series except the constant term, must vanish.

The Minimum Set of Singularities

A function, then, must have a singularity somewhere, possibly at infinity, and the same will be true of a function of two variables. In fact, such a function must have some singularities, and what we have not yet used is the fact that this function of two complex variables has to have a real physical interpretation if it is to represent a scattering amplitude. It would be too technical to enter into the exact limitation on the function provided by this, but perhaps a good analogy would be provided by considering again the functions of a single variable. The series which we were talking about in our examples were series of numbers which represented a function which was real when the variable was real, and if we limit ourselves to series of this kind then we can see that all the coefficients of the series must be real ones. If such a series has a singularity at the point z say, it follows that it will have another singularity at the point $\bar{z}$, so that we can say that for a series which is real on the real axis (real here means a complex number in which the coefficient of i is 0), either there is a singularity on the real axis which would have some sort of physical significance, or else there is a pair of singularities. In any case in a particular physical circumstance there will be a minimum set of singularities which the function must have. For example, if the physical circumstances were such that there could not be a singularity on the real axis then this minimum set of singularities would be at least two in number.

The situation with two complex variables is considerably more complicated, but it is generally believed that there is a minimum set of singularities, which is allowed by the physical conditions of the problem; the assumption made is that the scattering amplitude is an analytic function of the invariants which has only the singularities which are absolutely required by the physical restrictions. No other singularities are to be introduced. It is a most surprising thing that if we make this assumption about the scattering amplitude then, at least in the case of the strong interactions of particles, we get a number of results which agree well with experiment. We are able to make various calculations which would have been difficult or, indeed, completely unclear if we tried to tackle them by field theory.

It is interesting to notice that this development in elementary particle theory could have been foreshadowed a long time ago if the full detail of analytic continuation had been realised at the time. The way of dealing with the collision processes which we have described here is derived in general idea from that of Heisenberg, and Heisenberg has stressed for the past thirty years the importance of constructing a quantum mechanics in which only such observable quantities as momenta, energy, and scattering amplitudes arise, and from which we exclude all purely theoretical quantities about which we can really know nothing.

Heisenberg had considerable success in formulating the methods of doing this, and everything was expressed in terms of a scattering quantity. But unfortunately his theory was quite impotent because it could not calculate, within itself, the quantities from which everything was to be derived; it had to go back to conventional field theory or some such means for calculating these quantities. The reason why this was impossible for Heisenberg was because of the failure to realise that, with analytic continuation, one had to consider the scattering quantities as depending upon the momenta and energy as complex variables. One had to consider them defined over the whole complex range for these variables, and then one had also to require that only the minimum set of singularities was to occur. With these requirements the scattering quantities could be calculated. Heisenberg had the basic principles of the approach in 1943, but later, because of the difficulty of performing the calculations, he gave it up and tried a different approach.

The Present Situation

It would be misleading to leave the reader with the impression that all the problems of elementary particles, or even all the problems of strong interactions are solved by this approach. At present the whole situation is in a very fluid state. What I have been putting forward here as statements of how the thing should be done are really tentative proposals, which have only been carried out in detail in one or two cases. But there is every confidence amongst the workers in the field that when these proposals can be carried out in more complicated cases, which is a thing which may require very heavy calculation indeed, good results will be obtained there as in the cases which have been considered already. An example of an experimental result of very considerable importance, which results from discussions like this, will be described shortly.

We have been considering here the last of our examples of environment in physics. We began by considering the environment in Newtonian mechanics, and then we saw that we must take account of the varying time reckonings, and so have a more complicated environment in relativistic mechanics. When we came to consider elementary particles, this more complicated environment was already there, because everything has to be considered in a relativistically invariant manner, but over and above that there is a little more to be said. In ordinary relativistic mechanics we are dealing with ordinary macroscopic particles which are acted on by electro-magnetic fields or other forces of some kind. Of course these forces also constitute part of the environment in a particular problem, but the environment which we were discussing was the one which was common to all problems, and which was provided by the set of inertial observers who connected their measurements by means of Lorentz transformations. Now in the case of the elementary particles, because our information is derived entirely by collision processes, we can say that, in one sense, the environment for these particles is very much simpler. There is no longer any question of electro-magnetic fields or gravitational fields; to a high degree of approximation, the environment that a particle sees is simply the other particle which it hits, and with which it enters into a complicated interaction from which two other particles appear. Because of this peculiar environment of a much simpler kind than the ones which arise for macroscopic particles, there is complete symmetry between particle and environment, and this symmetry has to be incorporated into the theory. The way of incorporating it is to require that the scattering amplitude is not changed when the ingoing and outgoing particles are interchanged in any way. In order that this should be able to be expressed mathematically, we are forced to define the scattering amplitude in terms of complex energies and momenta.

It is reasonable to ask, does this new approach give us anything really worth while that we have not found already, perhaps by experiment? The answer is that it does, and this is more than could be said of the conventional field theory treatment. We have noticed that an analytic function must have singularities, and indeed we have used this fact by requiring that the scattering amplitude should have the minimum set of singularities. Now in a particular physical circumstance we can ask "what is the significance of these minimum singularities?" and by testing our methods on particular models we find that to each singularity there corresponds a particle.

To be more precise, there is a singularity in the scattering amplitude for any channel at the square of the mass of a single particle with the same properties as the channel. An example will make this clear. Consider *Figure 50*, which describes possible reactions between two nucleons and two π-mesons. In Channel I there is a positive charge on each side, one heavy particle (baryon number 1) and no strange particles (zero strangeness). The lightest particle with charge 1, baryon number 1, and zero strangeness, is the proton, so the amplitude for Channel I has a singularity at $s_1 = m_p{}^2$. The next lightest are compound particles made of π^0 and p, or of π^+ and n and, since these may have various energies, their masses extend over a range from $(m_p + m_\pi)$ to infinity, and do not occasion a point singularity.

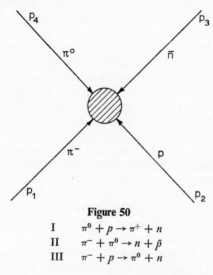

Figure 50

I $\pi^0 + p \rightarrow \pi^+ + n$
II $\pi^- + \pi^0 \rightarrow n + \bar{p}$
III $\pi^- + p \rightarrow \pi^0 + n$

In Channel II, on the other hand, no particle is known with charge -1, baryon number 0 and strangeness 0, so that there is no singularity, but the non-zero range of the scattering amplitude extends from $4m_\pi^2$ to infinity. (Channel III has the same singularities as Channel I, if we neglect the small mass difference between proton and neutron.)

The Phase-space Factor

The considerations which we have just described have led to a huge increase in the number of elementary particles which have to be considered. How this has come about will be made clear by considering the detailed investigation which led to the discovery in 1961 of the ω-meson, an uncharged particle which decays into 3 π-mesons according to

$$\omega \rightarrow \pi^+ + \pi^- + \pi^0.$$

Before we can do this we shall need to be a little more careful about defining the scattering amplitude. Let us take the case in which two particles are scattered, their initial energies and momenta being E_1, E_2, p_1 and p_2, and they become a number, n, of particles of energies and momenta E_j', $p_j'(j = 1, 2 \ldots n)$. Then quantum mechanics leads to a definite chance of any initial state i becoming a final state f, which we write as $P(i \rightarrow f)$, i and f being given in terms of the initial and final energies and momenta. Since there must always be *some* final state, the sum of $P(i \rightarrow f)$ over all possible f's is unity.

Notice that the form of $P(i \rightarrow f)$ is restricted by conservation of energy and momentum; in fact $P(i \rightarrow f)$ is zero unless

$$E_1 + E_2 = E_1' + E_2' + \ldots + E_n',$$
$$P_1 + P_2 = P_1' + P_2' + \ldots + P_n'.$$

To ask for the calculation of $P(i \rightarrow f)$ is, however, hopelessly ambitious. It is like the corresponding problem, in classical gas dynamics, of solving the equations of motion completely, so that for each one of some 10^{20} particles in a certain volume we can say what its position and momentum will be. Not only is this hopelessly ambitious; it is also physically useless, since we are only interested in averaged results over a large number of particles. In the same way here we ask, not for some individual $P(i \rightarrow f)$, but for $P(i \rightarrow F)$ where F is some given *set* of final states f. Clearly $P(i \rightarrow F)$ is the sum of $P(i \rightarrow f)$ for all f in the set F, and there will be no contribution to this sum except from states satisfying the equations of conservation of momentum and energy above.

There will then be a contribution to $P(i \rightarrow F)$ from all those states f satisfying the conservation equations. What contribution each of these states makes depends on the specific mechanism assumed for the scattering process; in any case it is hard to find. However, as in all statistical theories, if we average over a large number of possibilities, the specific mechanical details tend to become much less important, and the major contributor to the form of $P(i \rightarrow F)$ is the *volume of phase-space factor* i.e. the sum of *equal* contributions from all the states satisfying the conservation equations. Of course this will only be the case if the other factor—which is essentially the scattering amplitude—is fairly smoothly varying; a singularity in the scattering amplitude will show up as a failure of the statistical theory.

There is a close analogy to this way of procedure in ordinary statistics, e.g. of the population of a country. We could plot the number of members of the population (or the proportion) with a given height, obtaining a curve like the upper one in *Figure 51*, to which the lower curve in *Figure 51* is a serviceable approximation.

But now suppose we seek corresponding curves, first classifying the population by length of hair. The original statistical assumption (smoothly varying scattering amplitude) would correspond in this case to the same curve for each sub-class. But in fact we should

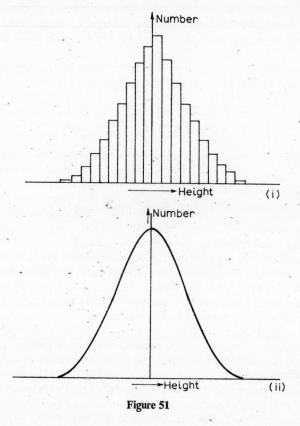

Figure 51

find that the longer the hair the more the peak of the curve is displaced to the left, because the sub-classes with longer hair tend to contain more women, whose average height is less.

Two Final Particles

It is rather a technical matter to calculate the phase-space factor, but we can give a good idea of its calculation in the particular case of 2 final particles, and this is a guide to its general nature. Since there is initially (and finally) two particles, we can choose

$$p_1 + p_2 = 0,$$

so that

$$p_1' + p_2' = 0$$

and the final momenta can be taken as $p_1' = p$, $p_2' = -p$. The phase-space depends on the initial energy $E_1 + E_2$, which we can call E, and it also depends on the masses m_1, m_2 (say) of the outgoing particles. (We did not mention this dependence before for simplicity.) The phase-space factor is therefore proportional to the volume of the set of final states which are such that

$$E_1'^2 - p^2 = m_1^2, \; E_2'^2 - p^2 = m_2^2, \; E_1' + E_2' = E,$$

i.e. such that

$$E_1'^2 - p^2 = m_1^2, \; (E - E_1')^2 - p^2 = m_2^2.$$

The variables here are now E_1' and p, the latter having both magnitude and direction. By subtraction

$$E_1'^2 - (E - E_1')^2 = E(2E_1' - E) = m_1^2 - m_2^2,$$

so that

$$E_1' = \frac{1}{2E} [m_1^2 - m_2^2 + E^2].$$

Then since E_1' is determined, the two equations above give the same result, $p^2 = E_1^2 - m_1^2$. Since, moreover, p has magnitude and

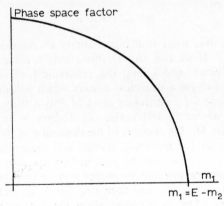

Figure 52

direction the number of values available to p, restricted by this equation, depends on the surface area of a sphere of radius $\sqrt{E_1^2 - m_1^2}$, i.e. $A = 4\pi p^2$.

However, for technical reasons, which it would lead us astray to explain here, the phase space factor is not equal to A but to $\dfrac{A}{pE}$. (This arises from the detailed definition of the scattering amplitude, which we have not given. Other definitions would be possible, including one leading to the space-phase factor A, and these would give slightly different statistics, but, as we shall see, essentially no difference to the final results.) The phase-space factor, as usually defined, is then $4\pi p/E$, that is,

$$\frac{2\pi}{E^2} \sqrt{[E^2 - (m_1 + m_2)^2][E^2 - (m_1 - m_2)^2]}.$$

The general variation of this factor as it depends on m_1, for given values of E and m_2, is shown in *Figure 52*.

For more particles than two the general form of variation of the phase-space factor is much the same, though the formulae are more complicated.

Mass Distribution

To see how to use the phase-space factor, consider the following concrete problem: in a process in which the final state is an n-particle state, let us group the n final particles into a group containing l particles, and one with the remaining $n - l$. We can call the total energy and momentum of the first group E' and p', and define its rest-mass M' by

$$M'^2 = E'^2 - p'^2.$$

Then we can ask, what is the probability of achieving particular values of M'? If we can answer this question assuming only the phase-space factor, and taking the mechanical effects as varying smoothly, we will get a statistical answer which will differ from the experimental one for a particular mass M only if there is any singularity in the scattering amplitude, i.e. if there is any elementary particle of mass M. On account of the definition of the phase-space factor, the factor for incoming energy and momentum E, p and masses m_1, m_2, . . . m_n can be analysed as the sum of the set of products of factors, one for an energy and momentum E', p' and masses m_1, m_2, . . ., m_l, and then one for E, p, and masses M', m_{l+1}, . . ., m_n. This is obvious, since the first factor gives the probability of particles of the first group arising with a particular rest-mass M', and then the second factor looks after the whole process.

Let us denote the phase-space factor for n particles by

$$R_n(E, p; \; m_1, m_2, \ldots, m_n).$$

Then this is given by a sum of products of the form

$$R_l(E', p'; m_1, m_2, \ldots m_l) \, R_{n-l+1}(E, p; \; M', m_{l+1}, \ldots m_n).$$

It is then obvious that the probability $p(M')$ of a given mass M' is given by

$$p(M') = \frac{R_l(E', p'; \; m_1, m_2, \ldots m_l) \, R_{n-l+1}(E, p; \; M', m_{l+1}, \ldots m_n)}{R_n(E, p; \; m_1, m_2, \ldots m_n)};$$

the total probability will then come out to unity, as it should. Thus $p(M')$ vanishes if

$$m_1 + m_2 + \ldots + m_l = M',$$

or if

$$m_{l+1} + \ldots + m_n = E - M',$$

and is positive between. This gives a general variation of the form shown in *Figure 53*. It is not necessary to calculate the form of the

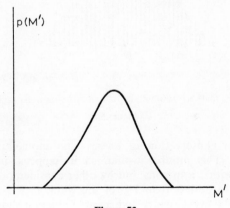

Figure 53

curve in more detail; it will in practice be given by the experimental results.

Discovery of the ω-meson

We wish now to describe the use of the phase-space factor in the discovery in 1961 (by Maglić, Alvarez, Rosenfeld and Stevenson) of the ω-meson. Various reasons had by then been given for expecting the existence of a heavy neutral meson, and these workers looked for a particle which could decay into 3 π-mesons. They did this by studying large numbers of bubble chamber photographs of proton-anti-proton annihilation, and looking at the mass distribution of triplets of π-mesons in the events

$$\bar{p} + p \rightarrow \pi^+ + \pi^+ + \pi^- + \pi^- + \pi^0.$$

In such a photograph the π^0, being neutral, leaves no track, so the experimenters had first to look at all the 2500 4-pronged events they had available, and calculate which of these (800 in number) involved

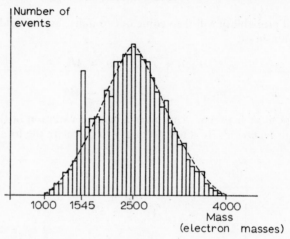

(The dotted curve is the phase-space factor)

Figure 54

(according to conservation of energy and momentum) at least 1 π-meson. (This number would, as it happens, include some interactions with 2 π-mesons, but by other considerations they estimated these to be less than 7% of the whole.) These 800 events lead to 4 × 800 events which give a curve like that shown in *Figure 54*. The smooth curve drawn through most of the points is then the phase-space factor. The deviations from it over most of its range are obviously simply statistical variations which arise because 3200 events is not enough for the statistics to be reliable. But the peak which occurs at 1544 electron masses is obviously quite a different matter. It is very high and narrow, corresponding to the effect of a singularity in the scattering amplitude at that mass value.

From the width of the peak it is possible to find the life time of the particle (the ω-meson). It is about 10^{-22} sec. Even if such a particle were to travel with the speed of light, it could travel only 10^{-12} cm before it decayed. Even apart from its being neutral (always a difficulty in observing particles), there is almost no hope of observing such a particle directly. The deviations from the phase-space factor have led to its discovery.

In a superficial way it is possible to see this discovery as an instance of the study of the environment. In this case the phase-space factor is used to define an environment, in the sense of a state of affairs in which nothing (i.e. no new particle) disturbs the experiment. Against this background the ω-meson can then make itself felt.

But it is also an instance of it in a much more profound way, since the peak arises from the singularities in the scattering amplitude. The existence of singularities is an indirect consequence of the substitution law, since an analytic function must have singularities somewhere. This law really expresses the fact that the whole environment in a scattering experiment is provided by the other particle—nothing else is relevant—and there is symmetry between particle and environment.

Conclusions

There is no hope at the moment of finishing the elementary particle story in any neat way. Still, two further facts arise from the discussion. Firstly, all the particles which arise in this way are on an equal footing, for one singularity is as good as any other; that is to say that no particles are more elementary than others, but all are equally elementary. This answers a query about whether some particles are of a more elementary nature than others, which had arisen in many people's minds before this approach was formulated. Secondly, many singularities are found to arise which had not previously been identified with particles. Where there is a particle there is certainly a singularity, but there appeared to be singularities where there were no particles. This has led to a considerable extension of our idea of a particle, in a way which we have exemplified by the ω-meson. It is embarrassing to say that there are singularities where there are no particles; it is more convenient to say, instead, that there is a particle wherever there is a singularity. By performing scattering experiments one can determine singularities in various circumstances and so determine constants of more and more particles like the ω-meson. In fact, one can say that the particles corresponding to all these singularities for which we thought there were no particles, are in fact simply very short-lived particles, which we would not have detected by "normal" methods. When we include all of the particles which have been observed in this way the number of particles comes to something like a hundred, as we said before. This simply points to the necessity for some more comprehensive theory than we have at the moment which will tell us which of these particles to concentrate our attention on, and to bring some order into this field which is becoming increasingly disordered.

Our discussion of the environment has, however, gone about as far as it could. Beginning with Newtonian absolute space and time, we considered next the set of Newtonian inertial observers. These observers are closely related to the actual observed universe by Mach's principle. But when we elaborate the way of setting up the inertial frames in more detail we find this environment much richer than we had expected, with many experimental consequences, particularly in the microscopic field. The next step is a very bold one; it is rather like the step to special relativity, which took account of the essential limitation on our experimental information caused by light moving with a finite velocity, and yet being the fastest signal available. The information about elementary particles must still be consistent with this limitation and also with the uncertainty principle. But, more than that, all our information comes from scattering experiments, and in these we can refine the environment even further. Each particle in a scattering experiment has its behaviour determined only by the other particle; moreover, in this simple situation, there is symmetry between particle and environment. This symmetry, as we have seen, has numerical consequences, leading to an enormous increase in the number of elementary particles observed. Each further step in our investigation of the environment has led to a more simplified and abstract version of it; it is hard to see how the process can be carried much past the present point.

INDEX

Date Due